D0926223

ACIDS, BASES, AND THE CHEMISTRY OF THE COVALENT BOND

Selected Topics in Modern Chemistry

SERIES EDITORS

Professor Harry H. Sisler
University of Florida
Gainesville, Florida

Professor Calvin A. VanderWerf
Hope College
Holland, Michigan

BREY–*Physical Methods for Determining Molecular Geometry*
CHELDELIN AND NEWBURGH–*The Chemistry of Some Life Processes*
EYRING AND EYRING–*Modern Chemical Kinetics*
HILDEBRAND–*An Introduction to Molecular Kinetic Theory*
KIEFFER–*The Mole Concept in Chemistry*
MOELLER–*The Chemistry of the Lanthanides*
MORRIS–*Principles of Chemical Equilibrium*
MURMANN–INORGANIC COMPLEX COMPOUNDS
O'DRISCOLL–*The Nature and Chemistry of High Polymers*
OVERMANN–*Basic Concepts of Nuclear Chemistry*
ROCHOW–*Organometallic Chemistry*
RYSCHKEWITSCH–*Chemical Bonding and the Geometry of Molecules*
SISLER–*Electronic Structure, Properties, and the Periodic Law*
SISLER–*Chemistry in Non-Aqueous Solvents*
SONNESSA–*Introduction to Molecular Spectroscopy*
STRONG AND STRATTON–*Chemical Energy*
VANDERWERF–*Acids, Bases, and the Chemistry of the Covalent Bond*
VOLD AND VOLD–*Colloid Chemistry*

ACIDS, BASES, AND THE CHEMISTRY OF THE COVALENT BOND

To my good friend
Vicki Wendell

CALVIN A. VANDERWERF

Hope College
Holland, Michigan

Cal VanderWerf

VAN NOSTRAND REINHOLD COMPANY
New York Cincinnati London Toronto Melbourne

Van Nostrand Reinhold Company Regional Offices:
Cincinnati New York Chicago Millbrae Dallas

Van Nostrand Reinhold Company International Offices:
London Toronto Melbourne

Copyright © 1961 by LITTON EDUCATIONAL PUBLISHING, INC.

Library of Congress Catalog Card Number: 61-18046

All rights reserved. No part of this work covered by the copyright hereon may be reproduced or used in any form or by any means —graphic, electronic, or mechanical, including photocopying, recording, taping, or information storage and retrieval systems— without written permission of the publisher. Manufactured in the United States of America.

Published by Van Nostrand Reinhold Company
450 West 33rd Street, New York, N. Y. 10001

10 9 8 7 6

FOREWORD

To the Student

Chemistry is fun!

And one of the greatest pleasures and satisfactions in the study of chemistry is the intellectual game of expanding horizons—of broadening concepts—so that more and more facts and figures can be interpreted, correlated, systematized, and *remembered* on the basis of fewer and fewer general principles.

This book is just such a game.

It leads you step-by-step in logical fashion to broader and broader concepts of the nature and function of acids and bases—until finally all polar reactions at the covalent bond come within the scope of the generalized acid-base concepts.

Nothing is more fundamental to all of chemistry. And nothing is more useful in helping you to learn, to understand, to appreciate, and to remember chemical reactions—and what really goes on in them. For actually we are dealing not with acids and bases alone, but rather with the heart of chemistry, the relationship between structure and chemical properties.

Our purpose is to develop a true appreciation of the relationship between electronic structure and reactivity, so that we will be able to predict the chemical reactions of a host of compounds simply on the basis of electronic structure.

For you, our hope is that these unifying concepts will breathe fresh meaning into chemistry, will point up all kinds of new relationships, and will simplify your problem of mastering chemistry by organizing for you a vast body of chemical information.

As you tie the facts of general chemistry together into handy conceptual bundles and as you lay the foundation for truly successful understanding and mastery of analytical and organic chemistry, we trust that this book will prove an invaluable aid. The last two chapters, particularly, will be especially helpful before you begin to study organic chemistry.

I enjoyed writing this book. I trust that you will enjoy studying it—and that it will add to your appreciation and enjoyment of all of chemistry.

To the Teacher

Can any assignment on today's college campus or in the contemporary high school be more challenging than that of teaching general chemistry!

Keeping pace with a dynamic science in its thrilling process of explosive growth is a stern but exhilarating challenge. And with it goes this problem forever inherent in the teaching of general chemistry: somehow we must teach at one and the same time (1) the inspiring intellectual constructions which we call the principles of general chemistry, (2) the background of experimental fact upon which they rest, (3) many of the facts and figures which illustrate them, and finally (4) the vast body of information which these principles tie together into a logically unified whole.

In our attempt to keep pace, and in our endeavor to present thoroughly those highly quantitative aspects of chemistry whose mastery can be so objectively measured, we often discover that one of the most useful of all qualitative principles which lies at the very heart of chemistry comes out second best—*the relationship between structure and properties.* And it happens that this concept, fundamental and useful as it is, is particularly difficult to develop in logical, convincing fashion at the same time that we must teach the facts upon which it rests and which it explains and unifies. The nature of our over-all task in the basic course is often such that we can hardly present the relationship between structure and properties in anything but a fragmentary, disjointed, piecemeal fashion. The unhappy result is that the picture the student carries with him is likely to be blurred.

This pocket text is designed to clear this picture. It develops in logical and lively step-by-step sequence, the concept of the relationship between covalent bond structure and, in the very broadest sense, acid-base properties. My aim is to bring the student to the point where, from a study of the structure of an individual covalent molecule, he can predict how that molecule *must* react—how its bonds are made or broken. And in the process I hope to organize with the student a vast body of significant chemical information. Nothing is more fundamental—for the making and breaking of bonds *is* chemistry—and to most students nothing is more generally useful, more intriguing, and more satisfying than a true understanding of the role of electronic structure in dictating the mechanisms of reactions.

No textbook can be worth its ink unless it is written to help someone. This auxiliary text is written directly and specifically for many people whom I know well:

(1) my students in general chemistry who are struggling to find true meaning in the broad, unifying, and simplifying principles of structure-property relationships;

(2) my students just beginning a course in organic chemistry who feel that somehow there is a wide gap between what they do know and what they would like to know about electronic structure and chemical reactivity;

(3) the many progressive and dedicated high school teachers who are challenging the notion that hydrogen ion is H^+;

(4) high school students who plan to continue their study of chemistry in college;

(5) the chemist, academic and non-academic, in other areas of specialization, to whom organic chemistry just doesn't make sense;

(6) organic research chemists, trained in an earlier generation, who find contemporary organic terminology totally confusing; and

(7) graduate students who desire to strengthen the conceptual foundation upon which their advanced learning rests.

I should like to thank the many inspiring teachers of chemistry, both high school and college, who in NSF Summer Institutes over the country have helped me to sharpen and focus many of the ideas presented in this short text. My sincere appreciation goes to Dr. Arthur W. Davidson and Dr. Earl S. Huyser, who read the manuscript and made valuable suggestions for its improvement, and to Mr. John Hart for his superb editorial assistance.

CALVIN A. VANDERWERF

Lawrence, Kansas
October, 1961

CONTENTS

chapter one

CLASSIFICATION OF REACTIONS AT THE COVALENT BOND

(or, Chemistry is Two-Thirds as Complex as Gaul)

All the chemistry of covalent compounds is two-thirds as complex as Gaul. For, although Caesar himself reported that Gaul was divisible into *three* parts, all the reactions of covalent compounds can be divided into just *two* broad fundamental types—*free radical reactions* and *polar reactions*. Most reactions can be classified rather sharply into one category or the other. The grouping of chemical reactions on the basis of the route or mechanism by which they proceed has become one of the most powerful intellectual tools of the modern chemist as he seeks to organize the terrain and extend the boundaries of existing chemical knowledge.

Free Radical Reactions

A chemical reaction is a change in which bonds between atoms or ions are formed, or broken, or both. To classify the reactions of covalent molecules, consider the simple case of the formation or breaking of a single covalent bond between two atoms or groups of atoms, A and B.

Actually, there are just two fundamentally different routes or mechanisms by which this bond can be formed or broken. In the first of these, the bond can be formed or broken in such a way that A supplies or retains one electron of the shared pair and B supplies or retains one electron of the shared pair:

$$A\cdot + \cdot B \rightleftharpoons A:B$$

This notation is not meant to imply that A· and ·B are necessarily either the initial reactants or the final products of the reaction, but only that the formation or breaking of the bond between A and B is an *electron-pairing–electron-unpairing* type reaction. This type of reaction usually involves intermediates which contain an unpaired electron. Any atom, group of atoms, or ion that contains one or more unpaired electrons is called a *free radical.* Hence, this type of reaction, in which electrons are paired or unpaired, is called a *free radical reaction* and proceeds by a *free radical mechanism.*

Free radical reactions show certain characteristics, one or more of which may be observable in a specific case. They

(1) frequently occur in the gas phase, often show induction periods and proceed by chain mechanisms, at times explosively,
(2) are often initiated by light, heat, or reagents which contain unpaired electrons, such as oxygen and decomposition products of peroxides,
(3) are inhibited by substances such as hydroquinone which are known to react readily with free radicals, and
(4) are rarely acid- or base-catalyzed, and their rate is usually independent of the polarity of the medium.

Many combustion and other oxidation reactions and many electrolytic reductions involving covalent compounds, as well as most polymerizations, are free radical reactions. The heat-initiated combustion of methane and the light-induced reaction of hydrogen with chlorine to produce hydrogen chloride are specific examples:

$$CH_4 + 2O_2 \rightarrow CO_2 + 2H_2O$$

$$H_2 + Cl_2 \rightarrow 2HCl$$

At ordinary temperatures in the absence of light, a mixture of hydrogen and chlorine reacts, if at all, only very slowly. In sunlight, however, the two gases combine with explosive violence. Why the difference? Chlorine molecules absorb light of a certain wave length and are dissociated into high energy chlorine atoms or free radicals:

$$:\ddot{\underset{..}{Cl}}:\ddot{\underset{..}{Cl}}: \xrightarrow[\text{energy}]{\text{radiant}} :\ddot{\underset{..}{Cl}}\cdot + \cdot\ddot{\underset{..}{Cl}}:^{*}$$

At any moment, in the sunlight, a minute fraction of the chlorine molecules is dissociated into chlorine atoms. The highly reactive chlorine atoms or free radicals react instantaneously with hydrogen molecules to give hydrogen chloride and energetic hydrogen atoms or free radicals:

$$:\ddot{\underset{..}{Cl}}\cdot + H:H \rightarrow H:\ddot{\underset{..}{Cl}}: + \cdot H$$

The highly reactive hydrogen atoms or free radicals then react with chlorine molecules to give hydrogen chloride and chlorine atoms or free radicals:

$$H\cdot + :\ddot{\underset{..}{Cl}}:\ddot{\underset{..}{Cl}}: \rightarrow H:\ddot{\underset{..}{Cl}}: + \cdot\ddot{\underset{..}{Cl}}:$$

And now the cycle is repeated again and again, with explosive rapidity. This is an excellent example of a *chain reaction*, a reaction that involves a series of steps, each of which generates a reactive substance that brings about the next step. A general type of chain reaction is represented schematically in Fig. 1.1.

*In writing electronic structures, we shall follow the practice of using the symbol of an element to represent the entire atom except its valence electrons, which are shown as dots surrounding the symbol. Thus, to represent the chlorine atom, we write the symbol Cl surrounded by seven dots for the valence electrons.

Reaction:

$$RH + XY \longrightarrow RY + HX$$

Chain Sequence:

$$X\cdot + RH \longrightarrow HX + R\cdot \xrightarrow{XY} RY + X\cdot$$

Fig. 1.1. Schematic Representation of a Chain Reaction.

Polar Reactions

The second separate and fundamentally different mechanism by which a single covalent bond between A and B can be formed or broken may be represented as follows:

$$A^+ + :B^- \rightleftharpoons A:B, \text{ or}$$

$$A + :B \rightleftharpoons A:B \text{ (for a coordinate covalent bond)}$$

Again, this notation is not meant to imply that A^+ or A and $:B^-$ or $:B$ are necessarily either the initial reactants or final products of the reaction, but only that as the bond between A and B is formed or broken, the electron pair is contributed or retained exclusively by either A or B (in this case, by B). In such a reaction, the bonding electron pair remains intact, and the formation or breaking of the bond is an *electron-pair-sharing –electron-pair-unsharing reaction.* This type of reaction which involves electron-pair donors and electron-pair acceptors is called a *polar reaction* and is said to proceed by a *polar mechanism.* Various schematic representations of bond making and breaking reactions are shown in Fig. 1.2.

Polar reactions

(1) usually occur in solution, but can also take place on polar surfaces,
(2) are often catalyzed by acids or bases, and their rate is strongly influenced by the polarity of the solvent,

(3) are not affected by light, oxygen, or peroxides, and
(4) are rarely chain reactions.

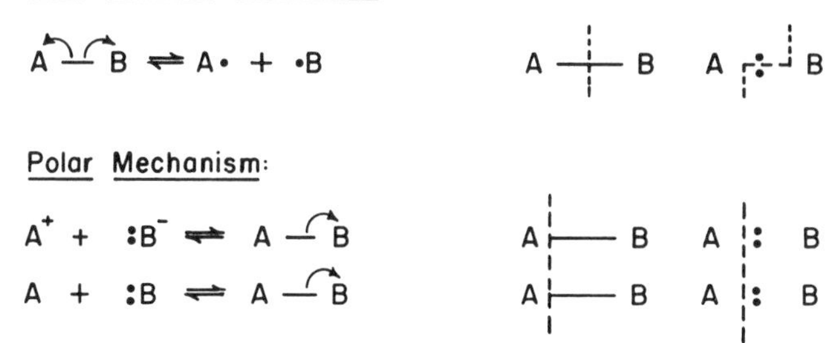

Fig. 1.2. Schematic Representation of Free Radical and Polar Bond Making and Breaking Reactions.

Included in the category of polar reactions are all the typical acid-base reactions of inorganic chemistry, such as the ionization reactions of acids and bases, neutralizations, and solvolyses, as well as the great bulk of the organic reactions which occur in solution. In fact, polar reactions may properly be called the acid-base reactions of chemistry, for all polar reactions come within the scope of the broadened acid-base concept. It is polar reactions with which the remainder of this book will be concerned. The tremendous contribution of the generalized acid-base concept is that it provides a consistent and logical basis for the classification, systematization, and interpretation of the whole host of reactions in chemistry of the electron-pair-sharing–electron-pair-unsharing or polar type, as well as a common basis for the understanding and correlation of inorganic and organic chemistry.

chapter two

THE BRØNSTED-LOWRY CONCEPT OF ACIDS AND BASES

(or, The Old Proton Transfer Game)

The early definitions of acids and bases were strictly experimental. An acid was a substance whose water solution: (1) turns blue litmus red, (2) neutralizes bases, (3) reacts with active metals with evolution of hydrogen, and (4) tastes sour. On the other hand, a base was a substance which in water solution: (1) turns red litmus blue, (2) neutralizes acids, (3) tastes bitter, and (4) feels soapy.

Limitations of the Arrhenius Concept

The brilliant Swedish chemical pioneer, Svante Arrhenius, whose ideas were as far ahead of his time as they are behind ours, proposed in 1887 that the characteristic properties of acids in water solution are the properties of hydrogen ion, H^+, and those of bases, the properties of hydroxide ion, OH^-. An acid was, therefore, a substance whose water solution contains an excess of H^+ ions, and a base, of OH^- ions.

It is apparent that the Arrhenius concept, applying as it does to aqueous solutions only, is exceedingly limited. His idea that the characteristic properties of bases listed in Fig. 2.1 are actually those of hydroxide ion was correct. He assumed, however, that such ionic bases as sodium and potassium hydroxide were ionized to produce hydroxide ion only when dissolved in water. Today, since we know that ionic compounds exist as ions even in the crystalline state, this view is no longer tenable.

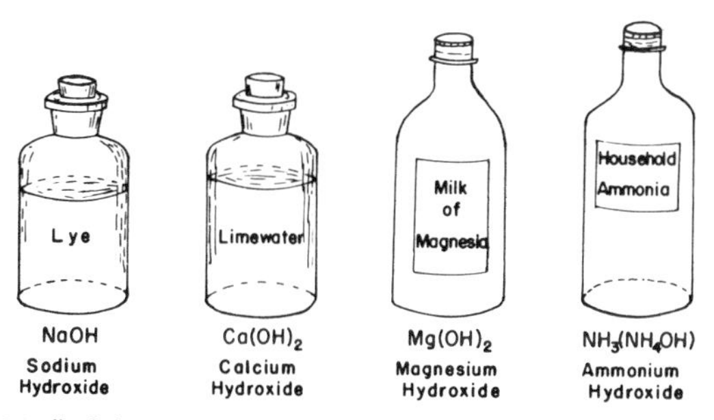

Fig. 2.1. All of these (1) turn red litmus blue, (2) neutralize acids, (3) taste bitter, and (4) feel soapy, because they contain an excess of hydroxide ion OH^-.

Arrhenius assumed further that the excess hydrogen ions in a water solution of an acid were formed by a simple equilibrium ionization of the acid as it dissolved in the water. Thus, for hydrogen chloride, Arrhenius postulated that the reaction consisted of a dissociation of some of the molecules into positive hydrogen and negative chloride ions, which existed in equilibrium with undissociated hydrogen chloride molecules:

$$HCl \rightleftharpoons H^+ + Cl^-$$

In the light of more recent knowledge, however, this interpretation is suspect on two counts. First, a hydrogen ion (H^+), being nothing more than a proton, is unique among cations; it contains no electrons at all and its effective radius is only about 10^{-13} cm compared with 10^{-8} cm for other simple ions. It is certain that a proton, with its enormously high ratio of charge to radius, could not exist unhydrated in water solution, completely surrounded by water molecules, whose oxygen atoms, of course, bear a partial negative charge, as well as two unshared electron pairs (see p. 42).

In fact, approximate calculations show that the union of a proton with a water molecule would be exothermic to the extent of about 300,000 calories per mole and that the fraction of protons which would remain unhydrated in water solution would be roughly 10^{-190}. This is equivalent to saying that free hydrogen cation or proton simply does not exist in aqueous solution. The same conclusion holds for any other solvent whose molecules have unshared pairs of electrons, and these are the only solvents which normally give conducting solutions even with the strongest acids. It appears certain, therefore, that although the bare proton can be produced in a discharge tube or in nuclear reactions, and can exist in gaseous solutions at very low pressures, it cannot be responsible for the properties of acids in solution.

Secondly, the Arrhenius postulation that acids are ionized to form proton flies in the face of all we now know about atomic and molecular structure. The filled first shell, with its single orbital, holds two electrons (electronic configuration of helium, see page facing inside rear cover). This is the stable electronic configuration for hydrogen.

Hence, there could be no possible driving force in chemical reaction that would induce a hydrogen atom in hydrogen chloride to part with its share in the electron pair simply to form a bare proton. The simple ion which hydrogen tends to form through chemical reactions is not proton, H^+, but hydride ion, $H:^-$.

For the sake of convenience, knowledgeable chemists today sometimes represent the ionization of acids in solution as forming simple H^+. But, as with the taking of slight liberties in the use of good grammar or in the exhibition of good manners, such a practice is suspect unless we are certain that the offender really knows better.

The Ionization of Covalent Acids and Bases

If the hydrogen ion or proton cannot exist unhydrated in water solution, we can most logically represent the ionization of hydrogen chloride in water as involving actual reaction with water molecules:

$$HCl + H_2O \rightleftharpoons H_3O^+ + Cl^-$$

or, in electronic formulas,

$$H:\ddot{\underset{..}{Cl}}: + \overset{H\quad H}{\ddot{\underset{..}{O}}} \rightleftharpoons \left[\begin{matrix} H & & H \\ & \ddot{O} & \\ H & & \end{matrix}\right]^+ + :\ddot{\underset{..}{Cl}}:^-$$

This reaction is represented diagrammatically in Fig. 2.2. The H_3O^+ ion, because of its resemblance to ammonium ion

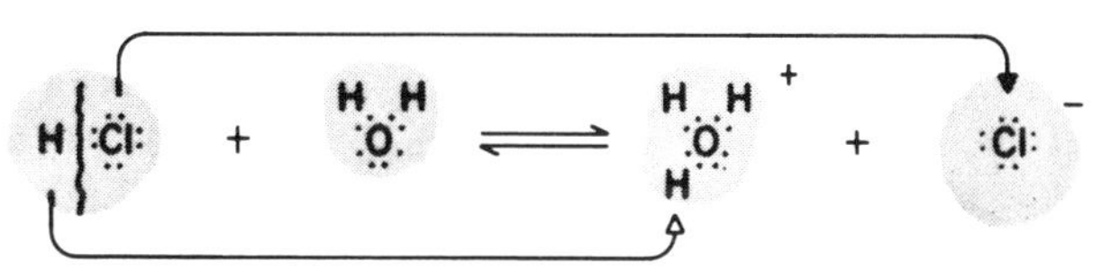

Fig. 2.2. The Ionization of Hydrogen Chloride in Water.

(NH_4^+), is called *hydronium ion.* Because water molecules are themselves associated through hydrogen bonds, it appears certain that each proton is associated with a variable number of molecules of water. Actually the hydronium ions in solution are probably $(H_5O_2)^+$, $(H_7O_3)^+$, $(H_9O_4)^+$, etc., the average extent of hydration being dependent upon the concentration and the temperature. The formula H_3O^+, however, is customarily used, as it is the simplest formula that denotes a hydrated hydrogen cation. In fact, the existence of hydronium ion, H_3O^+, in solutions of strong acids was proved conclusively in 1957 by means of infrared spectroscopy.

On this basis, the ionization in water of any monoprotic acid, HA, can be represented by the general equation

$$HA + H_2O \rightleftharpoons H_3O^+ + A^-$$

or, in electronic terms,

$$H:A + \begin{matrix} H \quad H \\ :\ddot{O}: \end{matrix} \rightleftharpoons \left[\begin{matrix} H \quad H \\ :\ddot{O}: \\ H \end{matrix}\right]^+ + :A^-$$

A classical acid, then, is really a compound which ionizes in water to give hydrated proton or hydronium ion, and the characteristic acid properties listed on page 6 and in Fig. 2.3 are actually those of hydrated proton or hydronium ion.

There are a number of covalent compounds, of which ammonia is the most familiar example, which in water solution exhibit the characteristic properties of bases, but which, according to conductivity and mole number values (i factors), are only very incompletely ionized. Such compounds are regarded as *weak* bases, because in water solution they give only relatively low concentrations of hydroxide ion. In the case of ammonia, the other product of the ionization reaction can be shown experimentally to be ammonium ion, NH_4^+. The equi-

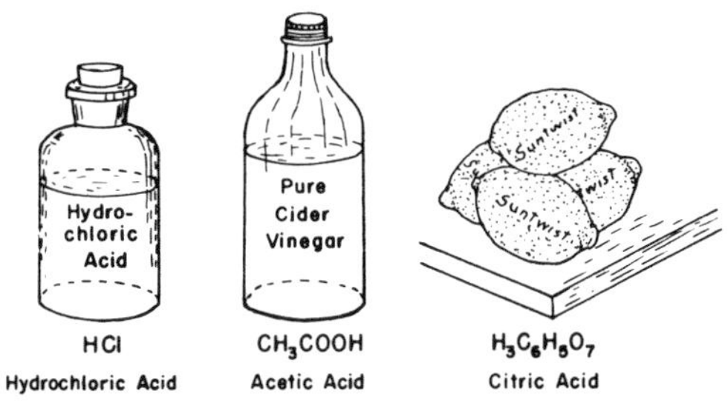

Fig. 2.3. All of these (1) turn blue litmus red, (2) neutralize bases, (3) react with active metals to produce hydrogen, and (4) taste sour, because they react with water to give hydronium ion, H_3O^+.

librium reaction involved in the ionization of ammonia in water can, therefore, be represented by the equation:

$$NH_3 + H_2O \rightleftharpoons NH_4^+ + OH^-$$

or, written electronically,

$$H:\overset{H}{\underset{\cdot\cdot}{\overset{\cdot\cdot}{N}}}:H + \overset{H\quad H}{\underset{\cdot\cdot}{\overset{\cdot\cdot}{O}}} \rightleftharpoons \left[H:\overset{H}{\underset{H}{\overset{\cdot\cdot}{\underset{\cdot\cdot}{N}}}}:H\right]^+ + [:\underset{\cdot\cdot}{\overset{\cdot\cdot}{O}}:H]^-$$

Other covalent compounds which similarly are weak bases ionize in the same way, and the general reaction can be represented as follows:

$$B + H_2O \rightleftharpoons BH^+ + OH^-$$

or, in electronic terms,

$$B: + \overset{H\quad H}{\underset{\cdot\cdot}{\overset{\cdot\cdot}{O}}} \rightleftharpoons [B:H]^+ + [:\underset{\cdot\cdot}{\overset{\cdot\cdot}{O}}:H]^-$$

The Brønsted-Lowry Concept of Acids and Bases

Careful scrutiny of the equation for the ionization of acids and of covalent bases reveals an interesting and significant fact. The function of an acid, such as hydrogen chloride, in its reaction with water, is the exact opposite of that of a base, such as ammonia. Whereas a molecule of the acid, hydrogen chloride, *donates* a proton to a water molecule, a molecule of the base, ammonia, *accepts* a proton from a water molecule.

This general idea has led to an important broadened concept of acids and bases. Independently, in 1923, J. N. Brønsted in Copenhagen and J. M. Lowry in Cambridge proposed that an *acid* be defined simply as *any substance that can donate a proton to any other substance.* A *base*, on the other hand, is *any substance that can accept a proton from any other substance.* In short, *an acid is a proton donor, a base is a proton acceptor.* This has come to be known as the Brønsted-Lowry, or simply the Brønsted, definition of acids and bases.

Conjugate Acid and Base Pairs

In terms of the Brønsted concept, the ionization of an acid, or of a covalent base, such as ammonia, is an equilibrium reaction involving two acid-base pairs. In the ionization of hydrogen chloride, for example,

$$HCl + H_2O \rightleftharpoons H_3O^+ + Cl^-$$

the hydrogen chloride *donates* a proton to water. Hydrogen chloride is, therefore, an acid, as we have already observed. Water, on the other hand, *accepts* a proton from hydrogen chloride, and in this reaction is therefore a *base*.

Now, consider the reverse reaction (from right to left), which at equilibrium is, of course, proceeding at the same rate as the forward reaction. In this reaction, the hydronium ion, H_3O^+, *donates* a proton to the chloride ion, Cl^-; hence it is an *acid*. Chloride ion, because it *accepts* a proton from the hydronium ion, is a *base*. It is significant that according to the Brønsted concept, many ionic species, as well as neutral compounds, can be acids or bases.

The acid hydrogen chloride, by losing a proton, forms the base chloride ion, which, in turn, by gaining a proton, can form the acid hydrogen chloride. This relationship can be represented as follows:

$$HCl \underset{+H^+}{\overset{-H^+}{\rightleftharpoons}} Cl^-$$

Such an acid-base pair, the members of which can be formed from each other mutually by the gain or loss of a proton, is called a *conjugate acid-base* pair. In general, we write

$$\underset{\text{Conjugate Acid}}{HA} \underset{+H^+}{\overset{-H^+}{\rightleftharpoons}} \underset{\text{Conjugate Base}}{A^-}$$

Similarly, the base water accepts a proton to form the acid hydronium ion, which in turn, by loss of a proton forms water.

$$H_2O \underset{-H^+}{\overset{+H^+}{\rightleftharpoons}} H_3O^+$$

Hydronium ion and water are, therefore, a second conjugate acid-base pair. This type of acid-base pair can be represented in general terms as follows:

$$\underset{\text{Conjugate Base}}{B:} \underset{-H^+}{\overset{+H^+}{\rightleftharpoons}} \underset{\text{Conjugate Acid}}{HB^+}$$

Hydrogen chloride is the conjugate acid of chloride ion, and chloride ion is the conjugate base of hydrogen chloride. If we arbitrarily designate hydrogen chloride as, say, acid_1, then it is convenient to designate its conjugate base, chloride ion, as base_1.

Similarly, water is the conjugate base of hydronium ion, and hydronium ion is the conjugate acid of water. So, if we designate water as base_2, we call its conjugate acid, hydronium ion, acid_2. This convention is illustrated for the ionization reactions of a number of acids:

	Acid_1	+ Base_2	$\rightleftharpoons$ Acid_2	+ Base_1
Hydrogen Chloride	HCl	+ H_2O	$\rightleftharpoons$ H_3O^+	+ Cl^-
Nitric Acid	HNO_3	+ H_2O	$\rightleftharpoons$ H_3O^+	+ NO_3^-
Sulfuric Acid	H_2SO_4	+ H_2O	$\rightleftharpoons$ H_3O^+	+ HSO_4^-
Perchloric Acid	$HClO_4$	+ H_2O	$\rightleftharpoons$ H_3O^+	+ ClO_4^-
Acetic Acid	CH_3COOH ($HC_2H_3O_2$)	+ H_2O	$\rightleftharpoons$ H_3O^+	+ CH_3COO^- ($C_2H_3O_2^-$)
Hydrogen Cyanide	HCN	+ H_2O	$\rightleftharpoons$ H_3O^+	+ CN^-

Relative Strengths of Acids and Bases

The *strength* of an acid, according to the Brønsted concept, is measured by its *tendency to donate a proton*; a *strong* acid is simply one which has a *strong* tendency to donate a proton. Similarly, the *strength* of a base is measured by its *tendency to accept a proton*; a *strong* base is one which has a *strong tendency to accept a proton*. The different strengths of acids and bases vary between extremely wide limits.

Water solutions of a few acids such as perchloric acid, hydrogen chloride, and nitric acid not only exhibit the characteristic properties of acids very strongly, but also have equivalent conductances and mole numbers comparable to those of ionic compounds at the same concentrations. It is apparent then that these acids at ordinary concentrations in water solutions are essentially completely ionized; in other words, the reactions in which they donate a proton to water proceed virtually to completion. These acids have a *relatively strong* tendency to donate a proton and are, therefore, *relatively strong acids*.

There are a number of acids, such as acetic acid and hydrogen cyanide, whose water solutions display the characteristic acid properties only weakly. Except in extremely dilute solutions, equivalent conductances are very small, and their mole numbers are only slightly greater than unity. In other words, these acids are only slightly ionized; they tend to donate a proton to water only to a limited extent. Because of their *relatively weak* proton-donating tendencies, these acids are considered *relatively weak acids*.

Other acids, such as sulfurous, nitrous and phosphoric acids are intermediate in strength between perchloric, nitric, hydrochloric and sulfuric acids, on the one hand, and acetic acid and hydrogen cyanide, on the other. They are regarded as moderately weak acids.

Two Important Axioms of the Brønsted Concept

Hydrogen chloride is a relatively strong acid since it tends to give up proton readily; conversely, chloride ion must necessarily be a weak base since it has little tendency to hold on to proton. This relationship suggests a highly significant axiom of the Brønsted concept:

> *the stronger an acid the weaker its conjugate base*, and
> *the stronger a base, the weaker its conjugate acid.*

Let's study this axiom in some specific cases. As a strong acid, hydrogen chloride is highly ionized, even in concentrated aqueous solution. At equilibrium, the reaction has proceeded far to the right, with most of the hydrogen chloride ionized to form hydronium and chloride ions. We can emphasize this fact by using arrows of unequal length to designate the forward and reverse reactions respectively:

$$\underset{\text{Stronger Acid}}{HCl} + \underset{\text{Stronger Base}}{H_2O} \rightleftharpoons \underset{\text{Weaker Acid}}{H_3O^+} + \underset{\text{Weaker Base}}{Cl^-}$$

In the equilibrium mixture, two acids, hydrogen chloride and hydronium ion, are competing to donate protons to a base. The hydrogen chloride wins; it is, therefore, the stronger acid. Similarly, two bases, water and chloride ion, are competing to accept protons. The water wins; it is, therefore, the stronger base. We see that the stronger acid, hydrogen chloride, has the weaker conjugate base, chloride ion. The stronger base, water, has the weaker conjugate acid, hydronium ion.

In the ionization of acetic acid in water, equilibrium is reached when the reaction has proceeded to the right only to a slight extent, with only a small fraction of the acetic acid present in the form of ions:

$$\underset{\text{Weaker Acid}}{CH_3COOH} + \underset{\text{Weaker Base}}{H_2O} \rightleftharpoons \underset{\text{Stronger Acid}}{H_3O^+} + \underset{\text{Stronger Base}}{CH_3COO^-}$$

Here, acetic acid and hydronium ion are the two acids competing to donate protons to a base. Hydronium ion triumphs; it is, therefore, the stronger acid. The bases, water and acetate ion, are competing to accept protons. Acetate ion triumphs; it is, therefore, the stronger base. Again, the stronger acid, hydronium ion, has the weaker conjugate base, water. The stronger base, acetate ion, has the weaker conjugate acid, acetic acid. Or conversely, we may say that acetate ion is a stronger base than chloride ion or water, because its conjugate acid, acetic acid, is a weaker acid than hydrogen chloride or hydronium ion.

You observe, also, that in each reaction when proton transfer has reached equilibrium, the reaction is found to favor the formation of the weaker acid and the weaker base. When the stronger acid donates proton, the conjugate base formed is the weaker of the two bases. When the stronger base accepts proton, the conjugate acid formed is the weaker of the two acids. In fact, it is axiomatic that

> *all proton transfer reactions run downhill to form predominantly the weaker acid and the weaker base.*

This important generalization applies not only to ionization but also to all other types of proton transfer reactions, such as neutralization and hydrolysis. In fact, whenever a potential proton donor and a potential proton acceptor come into contact with each other in solution, proton transfer or *protolysis* occurs to form a second acid and a second base. The extent of the protolysis, however, is determined by the relative strengths of the acids and bases involved. If the starting acid and base are much stronger than the products, protolysis will proceed far to the right before equilibrium is attained:

$$\text{STRONGER ACID} + \text{STRONGER BASE} \rightleftharpoons \text{Weaker Acid} + \text{Weaker Base}$$

If the starting acid and base are much weaker than the products, the reaction will proceed only slightly to the right:

$$\text{Weaker Acid} + \text{Weaker Base} \rightleftharpoons \text{STRONGER ACID} + \text{STRONGER BASE}$$

Acid-Base Charts

The gamut of acidity ranges all the way from such powerful acids as perchloric acid to such feeble potential acids as molecular hydrogen, itself, and methane. We can condense a large body of useful and interesting information by listing a series of acids, intermediate in strength between these two extremes, in order of relative strength. Such a list of acids, together with their conjugate bases, constitutes an acid-base chart, such as that shown on p. 19.

At least two general methods are widely employed in the comparison of relative acidity. The first of these is a comparison of proton-donating tendencies of different acids toward the same base. For moderately strong acids, water is commonly used as the base. As examples, the acid ionization constant or acidity constant, K_a (*a* for acidity), for acetic acid at 25°C is 1.8×10^{-5}; that for hydrogen cyanide is 4.0×10^{-10}.

$$CH_3COOH + H_2O \rightleftharpoons H_3O^+ + CH_3COO^- \quad K_a = 1.8 \times 10^{-5}$$
$$HCN + H_2O \rightleftharpoons H_3O^+ + CN^- \quad K_a = 4.0 \times 10^{-10}$$

Acetic acid is, therefore, a stronger acid than hydrogen cyanide; cyanide ion is a stronger base than acetate ion.

A second method is the competitive protolysis method. Here, one acid is added to the conjugate base of another and the equilibrium concentrations are determined experimentally. For example, when sodium ethoxide is added to water, we can demonstrate experimentally that the conjugate base of ethyl alcohol, ethoxide ion, reacts fairly completely with the water to form ethyl alcohol and hydroxide ion:

$$\underset{\text{Stronger Acid}}{H_2O} + \underset{\text{Stronger Base}}{C_2H_5O^-} \rightleftharpoons \underset{\text{Weaker Acid}}{C_2H_5OH} + \underset{\text{Weaker Base}}{OH^-}$$

Ethoxide ion is therefore a stronger base than hydroxide ion, and water, a stronger acid than ethyl alcohol.

An accurate experimental comparison of the relative strengths of two acids as feeble as molecular hydrogen and methane is extremely difficult, and, in fact, the order of acidity of those two exceedingly weak acids is a matter of dispute.

Perchloric acid is the strongest acid in the chart; its conjugate base, perchlorate ion, is consequently the weakest base in the list of bases. Methane and molecular hydrogen are the weakest of the listed acids; their conjugate bases, methide ion and hydride ion, are consequently the strongest bases. The remaining acids are listed between the two extremes in order of decreasing acidity, the bases in order of increasing basicity.

The most sweeping generalization implicit in the acid-base chart is this: The reaction of any acid with an equivalent quantity of any base below its conjugate base in the chart (stronger than its conjugate base) will proceed over 50 per cent to the right, to an extent depending qualitatively upon the slope of the line joining the acid and the base. Perchloric acid, and the base methide ion would react (don't try it!) with explosive violence, and essentially to completion, to give the infinitely weaker acid, methane, and weaker base, perchlorate ion. On the other hand, no significant reaction would be expected, for example, between the weak acid ammonia and the very weak base nitrate ion.

Phenol would be expected to react extensively with hydroxide ion, but not with bicarbonate ion; acetic acid, on the other hand, would give fairly complete reaction with either. This difference is used widely in organic chemistry to distinguish between carboxylic acids, RCOOH (R = H or an alkyl or aryl group) and phenolic compounds, ArOH (where Ar = an aryl group), and to separate compounds of the two types. Both carboxylic acids and phenols react with sodium hydroxide to form water-soluble, ether-insoluble salts:

$$\mathrm{RCOOH + OH^- \rightleftharpoons H_2O + RCOO^-}$$
$$\mathrm{ArOH + OH^- \rightleftharpoons H_2O + ArO^-}$$

With sodium hydrogen carbonate, however, only the carboxylic acids form the corresponding salts:

$$\mathrm{RCOOH + HCO_3^- \rightleftharpoons H_2CO_3 + RCOO^-}$$
$$\mathrm{ArOH + HCO_3^- \rightleftharpoons H_2CO_3 + ArO^-}$$

ACID-BASE CHART

Decreasing Acid Strength ↓ / Increasing Base Strength ↓

Conjugate Acid		Conjugate Base	
Name	Formula	Formula	Name
Perchloric acid	$HClO_4$	ClO_4^-	Perchlorate ion
Sulfuric acid	H_2SO_4	HSO_4^-	Hydrogen sulfate ion
Hydrogen chloride	HCl	Cl^-	Chloride ion
Nitric acid	HNO_3	NO_3^-	Nitrate ion
Hydronium ion	H_3O^+	H_2O	Water
Hydrogen sulfate ion	HSO_4^-	$SO_4^=$	Sulfate ion
Phosphoric acid	H_3PO_4	$H_2PO_4^-$	Dihydrogen phosphate ion
Acetic acid	CH_3COOH	CH_3COO^-	Acetate ion
Hexaaquoaluminum (III) ion	$Al(H_2O)_6^{+++}$	$Al(H_2O)_5(OH)^{++}$	Hydroxopentaaquoaluminum (III) ion
Carbonic acid*	H_2CO_3	HCO_3^-	Hydrogen carbonate ion
Hydrogen sulfide	H_2S	HS^-	Hydrosulfide ion
Ammonium ion	NH_4^+	NH_3	Ammonia
Hydrogen cyanide	HCN	CN^-	Cyanide ion
Hydrogen carbonate ion	HCO_3^-	$CO_3^=$	Carbonate ion
Phenol	C_6H_5OH	$C_6H_5O^-$	Phenoxide ion
Water	H_2O	OH^-	Hydroxide ion
Ethyl alcohol	C_2H_5OH	$C_2H_5O^-$	Ethoxide ion
Ammonia	NH_3	NH_2^-	Amide ion
Methylamine	CH_3NH_2	CH_3NH^-	Methylamide ion
Hydrogen	H_2	H^-	Hydride ion
Methane	CH_4	CH_3^-	Methide ion

*This is the position for carbonic acid based on its apparent acidity; it appears to be a rather weak acid because only a small fraction of dissolved carbon dioxide is in the form H_2CO_3.

Study of the acid-base chart serves to emphasize that the Brønsted acid-base concept is truly an extension of that of Arrhenius. The properties of acids and bases in water solution are the properties of hydronium and hydroxide ions, respectively. Compounds whose water solutions turn blue litmus red, neutralize alkalis, react with active metals with evolution of hydrogen, and taste sour are then definitely proton donors—in fact, they must be sufficiently powerful to donate proton, at least to a measurable extent, to water thus giving an excess of hydronium ion. All such compounds are, of course, stronger acids than water; the strong acids, which ionize extensively in water to give hydronium ion must be stronger acids than hydronium ion. Similarly, covalent compounds such as ammonia and amines, which give the properties associated with bases in the classical sense are then actually proton acceptors—in fact, they must be at least sufficiently strong to accept proton to some extent from the weak acid water to give an excess of hydroxide ion over hydronium ion.

Amphiprotic Substances

Another significant generalization emerges from the acid-base chart: many substances may act as acids in certain reactions and as bases in others. They are said to be *amphiprotic*.

The most familiar, and perhaps most interesting, amphiprotic compound is water. It acts as a base (proton acceptor) toward perchloric acid, hydrogen chloride, acetic acid and phenol, and as an acid (proton donor) toward ammonia, amines, ethoxide ion, and hydride ion. In fact, the amphiprotic nature of water is well illustrated in the extremely slight dissociation or self-ionization of water:

$$\underset{\text{Weaker Acid}}{H_2O} + \underset{\text{Weaker Base}}{H_2O} \rightleftharpoons \underset{\text{Stronger Acid}}{H_3O^+} + \underset{\text{Stronger Base}}{OH^-} \qquad K_w = 1.0 \times 10^{-14}$$

In pure water and in all aqueous solutions this equilibrium exists and must satisfy the equation:

$$\frac{[H_3O^+]\,[OH^-]^*}{[H_2O]^2} = K$$

But because in dilute solution the molar concentration of water $[H_2O]$ can be considered constant $\left(\frac{997 \text{ g/l}}{18.0 \text{ g/m}}\right.$ or about 55.4 moles per liter$\left.\right)$, the constant value $[H_2O]^2$ can be combined with the constant K to give K_w:

$$K[H_2O]^2 = K_w = [H_3O^+]\,[OH^-]$$

The very important constant K_w is called the *dissociation constant, ionization constant* or *ion product,* of water. At 25°C it has the value of 1.0×10^{-14}.

In pure water, all the hydronium and hydroxide ion must arise from the dissociation of water. This means that $[H_3O^+] = [OH^-]$, and if x mole of H_3O^+ is formed per liter, x mole of OH^- is also formed.

$$\begin{aligned} [H_3O^+]\,[OH^-] &= 1.0 \times 10^{-14} \\ (x)\,(x) &= 1.0 \times 10^{-14} \\ x^2 &= 1.0 \times 10^{-14} \\ x &= 1.0 \times 10^{-7} \end{aligned}$$

In pure water then the concentration of hydronium ion = the concentration of hydroxide ion = 1×10^{-7} molar. The ratio of H_2O concentration to that of H_3O^+ or OH^- is, therefore,

$$\frac{55.4 \text{ molar}}{1 \times 10^{-7} \text{ molar}} = 5.54 \times 10^8$$

*The bracketed formulas represent molar concentrations (moles per liter); for precise work a correction factor called an *activity coefficient* must be applied, to give the corrected concentration or *activity* of the species in question.

On the average, then, there is one H_3O^+ ion and one OH^- ion for each 5.54×10^8 or 554 million H_2O molecules. In aqueous solutions which show the characteristic acid properties, $[H_3O^+] > 1 \times 10^{-7}$ molar; in those which exhibit the familiar basic properties, $[OH^-] > 1 \times 10^{-7}$ molar.

Many ions, such as hydrogen sulfate ion, HSO_4^-, and hydrogen carbonate ion, HCO_3^-, are also amphiprotic. As indicated in the acid-base chart, sulfuric acid ionizes in two steps:

$$\begin{array}{cccc} \text{Acid}_1 & \text{Base}_2 & \text{Acid}_2 & \text{Base}_1 \\ H_2SO_4 + & H_2O \rightleftharpoons & H_3O^+ + & HSO_4^- \\ HSO_4^- + & H_2O \rightleftharpoons & H_3O^+ + & SO_4^= \end{array}$$

In the first step, hydrogen sulfate ion, HSO_4^-, acts as a base; in the second, as an acid.

The Leveling Effect

Since all protolysis reactions tend to run downhill, all the acids which are stronger than hydronium ion are extensively ionized in water to form the weaker acid hydronium ion. All the acids above hydronium ion in the acid list, for example, are essentially completely ionized in dilute aqueous solution. It is not surprising, therefore, that such strong acids as perchloric, sulfuric and nitric acids and hydrogen chloride all appear to have equal strengths in water solution, for the same acid—hydronium ion—is common to all such solutions.

This means that the apparent acidity in water solution of all very strong acids is reduced to the same mediocre level—that of the hydronium ion. This phenomenon is called the *leveling effect*. When a stronger acid than hydronium ion is added to water, it instantaneously donates a proton to water to form hydronium ion. Thus hydronium ion is the strongest acid which can exist in appreciable concentration in water solution, as shown schematically in Fig. 2.4.

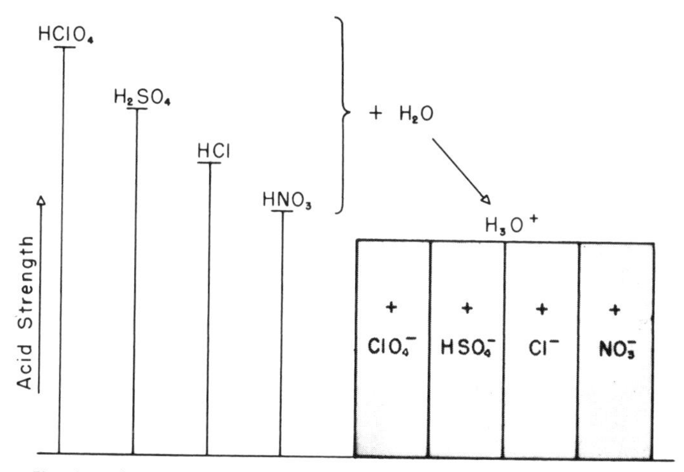

Fig. 2.4. The Leveling Effect of Water on Strong Acids. In aqueous solutions, all very strong acids donate proton to water and are leveled to the strength of hydronium ion.

The strongest acid that can exist in appreciable concentration in any solvent that can act as a base is the conjugate acid of that solvent. In acetic acid, that acid is $CH_3C(OH)_2^+$, in ammonia, NH_4^+, and in ethyl alcohol, $C_2H_5OH_2^+$.

As an amphiprotic solvent, water also exerts a leveling effect on strong bases. Consider what takes place when a stronger base than hydroxide ion is added to water. In order to select such a base, consider the fact that according to the Brønsted concept sodium hydroxide itself is not a base; it is an *ionic compound* or *salt** whose anion, hydroxide ion, happens to be a relatively strong base (the strongest base, in fact, which can exist in water solution). In all of the reactions of sodium hy-

*If this idea seems startling, consider the following series of salts: Na_2SO_4, NaCl, CH_3COONa, C_6H_5ONa, NaOH, C_2H_5ONa, $NaNH_2$, and NaH. Why should NaOH be singled out to be designated as a base?

droxide involving hydroxide ion, sodium ion, Na^+, is a "spectator" ion—a mere bystander, existing as Na^+ both before and after the reaction.

Where shall we look to find a stronger base than hydroxide ion? Simply select the conjugate base of a weaker acid than water. Since ethyl alcohol, ammonia, and hydrogen are all weaker acids than water, their conjugate bases, ethoxide ion ($C_2H_5O^-$), amide ion (NH_2^-), and hydride ion (H^-) are all stronger bases than the conjugate base of water (OH^-). This fact is highlighted in the acid-base chart.

Sodium amide, $NaNH_2$, is a crystalline, ionic compound, readily prepared by reaction of sodium with liquid ammonia, just as sodium hydroxide can be obtained from sodium and water. In the Brønsted concept, sodium amide is viewed simply as a salt whose anion is a strong base—a stronger base, in fact, than hydroxide ion. Now, when sodium amide is added to water, a vigorous reaction ensues with liberation of ammonia. The resulting solution shows all the classical basic properties; in fact, it is simply a solution of sodium hydroxide (and ammonia). The amide ion, as a stronger base than hydroxide ion, simply reacts almost completely with water to form hydroxide ion:

$$\underset{\text{Stronger Acid}}{H_2O} + \underset{\text{Stronger Base}}{NH_2^-} \rightleftharpoons \underset{\text{Weaker Acid}}{NH_3} + \underset{\text{Weaker Base}}{OH^-}$$

The strong bases ethoxide ion, in sodium ethoxide ($NaOC_2H_5$), and hydride ion, in sodium hydride (NaH), react with water to form hydroxide ion in the same way. In fact, hydroxide ion is the strongest base that can exist in any appreciable concentration in water solution. When a stronger base is added to water, it accepts a proton from water and its apparent basicity is reduced to the level of hydroxide ion. This is an example of the base leveling effect (see Fig. 2.5).

Again, we can generalize the fact by saying that the strongest base available in any solvent that can act as an acid is the

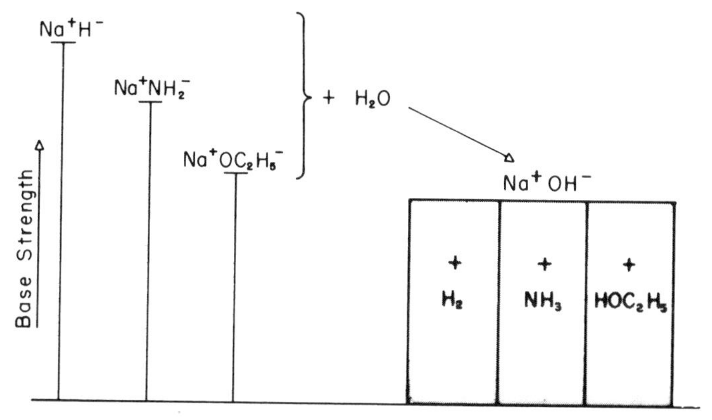

Fig. 2.5. The Leveling Effect of Water on Strong Bases. In aqueous solutions, all very strong bases are leveled to the strength of hydroxide ion (OH^-), for they react completely with water to produce OH^-.

conjugate base of that solvent. For acetic acid that base is acetate ion, for ethyl alcohol, ethoxide ion, and for liquid ammonia, amide ion.

The intrinsic acidity and basicity of solvents which can engage in proton transfer profoundly affect the usefulness of the solvent for reactions demanding strong acids or bases. In many organic reactions, for example, strong acid or base catalysts are required. Water cannot be used as a solvent in such reactions; in fact, its mere presence must be scrupulously avoided. For reactions involving or catalyzed by very strong bases or acids, the organic chemist often uses so-called *aprotic* solvents, which are relatively indifferent to proton transfer. Hexane (C_6H_{14}), benzene (C_6H_6), toluene ($C_6H_5CH_3$), chlorobenzene (C_6H_5Cl), nitrobenzene ($C_6H_5NO_2$), and carbon tetrachloride (CCl_4) are widely used aprotic solvents.

Neutralization in Aqueous Solutions

Any protolysis reaction which proceeds more than 50 per cent to completion may be thought of as a neutralization reaction in the sense that a stronger acid and a stronger base are "neutralized" to a weaker acid and a weaker base. The classical concept of neutralization, however, is more restricted. Classical neutralization in aqueous solution is a *protolytic reaction in which water is a product.* In fact, when strong acids are neutralized by ionic hydroxides in dilute aqueous solution, water is the *only* product.

When a dilute solution of a strong acid such as hydrogen chloride is added to a solution of an ionic hydroxide such as sodium hydroxide, in reality hydronium, chloride, sodium, and hydroxide ions are being mixed. Only the acid hydronium ion and the base hydroxide ion react:

$$\underset{\text{Acid}_1}{H_3O^+} + \underset{\text{Base}_2}{OH^-} \rightleftharpoons \underset{\text{Acid}_2}{HOH} + \underset{\text{Base}_1}{HOH}$$

The sole product is water, which is both the conjugate acid of the base hydroxide ion and the conjugate base of the acid hydronium ion. Because hydronium is a considerably stronger acid and hydroxide ion a considerably stronger base than water, the reaction proceeds essentially to completion to the right. The sodium and chloride ions are merely spectator ions. The equation shown represents the fundamental reaction—the reaction of hydronium ion with hydroxide ion to form water—that occurs when any strong acid is neutralized by any ionic hydroxide in water solution. Corroboration of this view is offered by the fact that the *heat of neutralization*—the heat evolved per mole of H_3O^+ ion and of OH^- ion reacting—for the reaction of any strong acid with any ionic hydroxide always has the same value, 13,360 cal at 25° C. When either the acid or base, or both, are weak, the value is different, suggesting that a different reaction is involved.

This is the case when a weak acid such as acetic acid is neutralized by an ionic hydroxide. Since very little of the acetic acid is ionized, the effective reaction is that between acetic acid, itself, and hydroxide ion:

$$\underset{\text{Acid}_1}{CH_3COOH} + \underset{\text{Base}_2}{OH^-} \rightleftharpoons \underset{\text{Acid}_2}{HOH} + \underset{\text{Base}_1}{CH_3COO^-}$$

Unlike the reaction between hydronium and hydroxide ions, this reaction does not proceed essentially to completion, because the acid acetic acid is not so strong as hydronium ion and the base acetate ion is not so weak as water. Hence, at equilibrium in the reaction of molar quantities of acetic acid and hydroxide, there is a measurable excess of hydroxide ion, and the solution turns red litmus blue. These facts are typical of the reaction between a weak acid and an ionic hydroxide.

Similar principles apply to the neutralization of weak bases, such as ammonia and amines, by strong acids, such as hydrogen chloride or nitric acid. The reaction of ammonia with a strong acid in aqueous solution is best represented by the equation

$$\underset{\text{Acid}_1}{H_3O^+} + \underset{\text{Base}_2}{NH_3} \rightleftharpoons \underset{\text{Acid}_2}{NH_4^+} + \underset{\text{Base}_1}{H_2O}$$

Again, this reaction does not proceed to completion and the concentrations of hydronium ion and ammonia remaining in solution at equilibrium are not insignificant. At the equivalence point, there is a definite measurable excess of hydronium ion, and the solution exhibits, at least weakly, the characteristic acid properties.

Neutralization in Non-Aqueous Solvents

Neutralization in water solution of a strong acid with a strong base is actually the reaction of the conjugate acid of water with the conjugate base of water to form water. In fact, the neutralization reaction typical of any protonic solvent is the reaction of its conjugate acid with its conjugate base to form the solvent itself. For ammonia, ethyl alcohol, acetic acid, and sulfuric acid, respectively, the typical neutralization reactions are shown in Table 2.1.

TABLE 2.1. Typical Neutralization Reactions for the Solvents Ammonia, Ethyl Alcohol, Acetic Acid, and Sulfuric Acid

$Acid_1$	+ $Base_2$		$Acid_2$	+ $Base_1$
NH_4^+	+ NH_2^-	$\rightleftharpoons$	NH_3	+ NH_3
$C_2H_5OH_2^+$	+ $C_2H_5O^-$	$\rightleftharpoons$	C_2H_5OH	+ C_2H_5OH
$CH_3C(OH)_2^+$	+ CH_3COO^-	$\rightleftharpoons$	CH_3COOH	+ CH_3COOH
$H_3SO_4^+$	+ HSO_4^-	$\rightleftharpoons$	H_2SO_4	+ H_2SO_4

Preparations of Weak Acids and Bases by Protolytic Reactions

For many decades, a classical maxim of chemists at all levels has been "to prepare a weak acid, add a strong acid to a salt of the weak acid." The rule is a good one, because when a strong acid is added to a salt of a weaker acid, the strong acid donates a proton to the conjugate base of the weak acid to form the weak acid. Thus, acetic acid, hydrogen cyanide, hydrogen sulfide, and carbonic acid are readily prepared by addition of sulfuric acid or hydrochloric acid (a water solution of hydrogen chloride) to their soluble salts:

$Acid_1$	$Base_2$		$Acid_2$	$Base_1$
H_3O^+	+ CH_3COO^-	$\rightleftharpoons$	CH_3COOH	+ H_2O
H_3O^+	+ CN^-	$\rightleftharpoons$	HCN	+ H_2O
H_3O^+	+ HS^-	$\rightleftharpoons$	H_2S	+ H_2O
H_3O^+	+ HCO_3^-	$\rightleftharpoons$	H_2CO_3	+ H_2O

Because hydronium ion is a stronger acid than any of those on the right, each reaction proceeds far toward the right. If their saturation solubilities are reached, gaseous hydrogen cyanide, hydrogen sulfide, and carbon dioxide (formed by the decomposition of carbonic acid) are evolved. Evolution of hydrogen sulfide and carbon dioxide upon the addition of a strong acid is recognized as a positive test for hydrosulfide (or sulfide) and hydrogen carbonate (or carbonate) ions, respectively.

These reactions are actually neutralizations, as one of the products in every case is water. Further, we observe experimentally that sodium hydrogen carbonate, for example, neutralizes strong acids almost as effectively as does sodium hydroxide.

Similarly, ammonium ion and alkylammonium (such as methylammonium) ions neutralize strong bases, with the formation of ammonia or the corresponding amine:

$$\underset{\text{Acid}_1}{NH_4^+} + \underset{\text{Base}_2}{OH^-} \rightleftharpoons \underset{\text{Acid}_2}{H_2O} + \underset{\text{Base}_1}{NH_3}$$

$$CH_3NH_3^+ + OH^- \rightleftharpoons H_2O + CH_3NH_2$$

Hydrolysis

The fact that the solution resulting from the addition of sodium amide to water turns red litmus blue (see p. 24) constitutes experimental proof that some base must have been introduced into the water. The base is the amide ion, which accepts a proton from water to form ammonia and hydroxide ion. This reaction is a specific example of the *hydrolysis* of a salt, or more strictly, of an anion. The hydrolysis of amide ion, like that of hydride and ethoxide ions, is an extreme case in that amide ion is a stronger base than hydroxide ion; its reaction with water is essentially complete and an equivalent amount of hydroxide ion is formed. Complete hydrolysis is characteristic of anions whose conjugate acids are weaker than water.

There are, however, many salts whose anions are weaker bases than hydroxide ion but which nevertheless give alkaline water solutions. These are the salts, such as sodium hydrogen carbonate, potassium cyanide, sodium acetate, and potassium carbonate, the conjugate acids of whose anions are relatively weak, but at least somewhat stronger acids than water. All these salts dissolve in water without any directly observable reaction, yet the resulting solution in each case turns red litmus blue. The ion responsible for this behavior is the anion; in each case the anion, although a weaker base than hydroxide ion, must accept proton from water, at least to a measurable extent, to afford an excess of hydroxide ion. Thus, when sodium acetate is dissolved in water, the salt (or, more strictly speaking, the acetate ion) undergoes very partial hydrolysis to form acetic acid and hydroxide ion:

$$\underset{\text{Acid}_1}{H_2O} + \underset{\text{Base}_2}{CH_3COO^-} \rightleftharpoons \underset{\text{Acid}_2}{CH_3COOH} + \underset{\text{Base}_1}{OH^-}$$

This reaction is the exact reverse of the neutralization of acetic acid with an ionic hydroxide (p. 26). In fact for any salt, hydrolysis (protolysis between an ion and water) is the exact reverse of neutralization (protolysis in which water is one of the *products*). We have already seen that the neutralization of acetic acid with an ionic hydroxide does not proceed essentially to completion (p. 27); we can now explain this fact from another standpoint by saying that the reverse reaction, the hydrolysis, occurs to at least a measurable extent. Since acetate ion is a weaker base than hydroxide ion—just as water is a weaker acid than acetic acid—the hydrolysis of acetate ion in sodium acetate proceeds to a limited extent.

A water solution of sodium chloride is neutral to litmus. Why does not chloride ion undergo hydrolysis? Simply because, like the conjugate bases of other strong acids, it is too weak as a base to accept a proton from water to any significant extent. Only anions that are relatively strong bases undergo hydrolysis. In fact, the effect of sodium acetate solution on red litmus is a direct indication that acetate ion is a relatively strong base, and constitutes the simplest experimental proof that acetic acid is a weak acid.

There are salts, such as ammonium and alkylammonium chlorides and sulfates, whose cations contain hydrogen, that exhibit weak acid characteristics in water. These salts must contain an ion that donates proton to water to a significant extent to form hydronium ion. In other words, ammonium and alkylammonium salts are slightly hydrolyzed:

$$\begin{array}{lcl} \text{Acid}_1 & \text{Base}_2 & & \text{Acid}_2 & \text{Base}_1 \\ NH_4^+ & + H_2O & \rightleftharpoons & H_3O^+ & + NH_3 \\ RNH_3^+ & + H_2O & \rightleftharpoons & H_3O^+ & + RNH_2 \end{array}$$

The ammonia (or amine) is competing with water for protons. Ammonia (or the amine) as the stronger base retains the lion's share. But the basicity of water is at least comparable to that of ammonia, and water captures a few protons, thus affording a sufficient excess of hydronium ions to give an acid test toward litmus. In fact, the litmus test applied to ammonium chloride constitutes simple experimental proof that ammonia is, after all, a rather weak base.

Salts whose cations are relatively strong acids and whose anions are relatively strong bases are easily decomposed, because of protolysis between the two types of ions. Ammonium acetate and ammonium carbonate (smelling salts) give an appreciable vapor pressure of ammonia even at room temperatures. This is due to the reactions

$$\begin{array}{lcl} \text{Acid}_1 & \text{Base}_2 & & \text{Acid}_2 & \text{Base}_1 \\ NH_4^+ & + CH_3COO^- & \rightleftharpoons & CH_3COOH & + NH_3 \\ NH_4^+ & + CO_3^= & \rightleftharpoons & HCO_3^- & + NH_3 \end{array}$$

Hydrolysis of Hydrated Salts

If aluminum chloride is added to water, hydrolysis occurs and the resulting solution is strongly acid. This is true for many salts and pseudo-salts, such as zinc chloride, stannic chloride, cupric sulfate, and platinic chloride, that contain a polyvalent metal. In fact, in general, the higher the oxidation state of the metal, the more extensive the hydrolysis.

Now it is well known that aluminum ion exists as a hydrate, probably $Al(H_2O)_6^{+++}$, in water. The slight tendency of water molecules to donate protons is undoubtedly greatly increased when the water molecules are attached to a highly charged cation, since there is a strong force of repulsion between the ion and the similarly positively charged proton. The hydrated aluminum ion would be expected to be a considerably stronger acid than water and to undergo partial hydrolysis:

$$\underset{\text{Acid}_1}{Al(H_2O)_6^{+++}} + \underset{\text{Base}_2}{H_2O} \rightleftharpoons \underset{\text{Acid}_2}{H_3O^+} + \underset{\text{Base}_1}{Al(H_2O)_5(OH)^{++}}$$

Similarly, for the hydrated zinc ion we may write

$$Zn(H_2O)_4^{++} + H_2O \rightleftharpoons H_3O^+ + Zn(H_2O)_3(OH)^+$$

Indicators

Most acid-base indicators such as litmus, methyl orange, and bromthymol blue are themselves conjugate acid-base systems, in which the conjugate acid differs sharply in color from its conjugate base. Each indicator undergoes a color change in water solution at a *p*H dependent upon the strengths of the acid and base in the conjugate system of the indicator. Often indicators are used to measure relative strengths of acids and bases in water solution.

Buffer Solutions

Solutions which resist marked changes in hydronium ion concentration when diluted or when acids or bases are added to them are called buffer solutions. An equimolar solution of acetic acid – sodium acetate is a buffer solution. When strong acid is added to the solution, the hydronium ions react with acetate ions to form acetic acid; when ionic hydroxide is added, the hydroxide ions react with acetic acid to form acetate ions:

$$\begin{array}{ccccccc} \text{Acid}_1 & & \text{Base}_2 & & \text{Acid}_2 & & \text{Base}_1 \\ H_3O^+ & + & CH_3COO^- & \rightleftharpoons & CH_3COOH & + & H_2O \\ CH_3COOH & + & OH^- & \rightleftharpoons & H_2O & + & CH_3COO^- \end{array}$$

In either case, the added hydronium ion or hydroxide ion is effectively neutralized, and the changes in hydronium and hydroxide concentrations are slight. Actually a mixture of any weak acid, somewhat stronger as an acid than water, with its conjugate base, acts as a buffer.

chapter three

ACIDITY, BASICITY, AND STRUCTURE

(or, "Need Two, from You"—"Have Pair, Will Share")

Any hydrogen-containing molecular or ionic species is a potential proton donor or Brønsted acid. But, as we have seen, acidity runs the gamut from powerful acids like $H_3SO_4^+$ to such feeble acids as CH_4. And potentially, any molecular or ionic species with an unshared electron pair is a proton acceptor or Brønsted base. But basicity runs the gamut from potent bases like CH_3^- to such weak bases as H_2SO_4.

What makes an acid an acid or a base a base? What structural features confer proton-donating or proton-accepting tendencies? As we explore these questions, we come to grips with one of the most intriguing and significant frontiers of modern chemistry—the relationship between structure and chemical properties.

Structure of the HCl Molecule

Consider the state of the hydrogen in hydrogen chloride. For hydrogen, the stable electronic configuration is that of helium, with two electrons in the valence shell (K shell) (see page facing inside rear cover). And in the HCl molecule, hydrogen does, indeed, have two electrons in its valence shell:

$$\mathrm{H : \underset{\cdot\cdot}{\overset{\cdot\cdot}{Cl}} :}$$

But the situation is not exactly as this electronic formula suggests. Chlorine has a much stronger *power of attraction for a shared electron pair* than does hydrogen. We say that chlorine is more *electronegative* or has a higher *electronegativity*.

What is the result? On the average, the bonding electron pair in hydrogen chloride is not shared equally between the hydrogen and chlorine atoms. Rather it is displaced away from the hydrogen toward the more electronegative chlorine. Because of this electron displacement, the bond is said to be *polar*. The chlorine end of the molecule has a *high electron density* and is somewhat *negatively charged*. The hydrogen end has a *low electron density* and is *positively charged*. Using the symbols δ^+ and δ^- to represent partial positive and partial negative charges, we can show this unequal distribution of charge as follows:

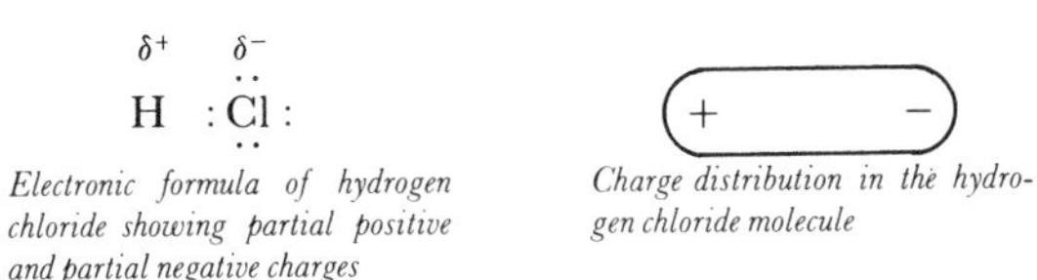

Electronic formula of hydrogen chloride showing partial positive and partial negative charges

Charge distribution in the hydrogen chloride molecule

The hydrogen chloride molecule as a whole is electrically neutral, because the positive and negative charges within each molecule are exactly balanced. Nevertheless, the molecule is electrically unsymmetrical. Such molecules, in which the centers of positive and negative charge do not coincide, but are separated by some *finite* distance, are called *polar* molecules or dipoles. In the hydrogen chloride molecule the hydrogen atom is the positive end of the dipole and the chlorine atom is the negative end.

The positively charged hydrogen atom is electronically deficient. It is susceptible to attack by any species, which can share a pair of electrons. Its motto is, "Need two, from you." (Fig. 3.1). And such a hydrogen becomes transferable as a

Fig. 3.1. An acid can accept, and a base can share, a pair of electrons.

proton. For when the possibility of a better share in an electron pair presents itself, the hydrogen accepts it, leaving the former bonding electron pair behind.

When hydrogen chloride comes into contact with ammonia, for example, the hydrogen accepts a share in the unshared pair on the nitrogen atom of the ammonia molecule to form ammonium ion, leaving the chlorine with the bonding pair behind as chloride ion (as shown in Fig. 3.2).

General Structural Nature of Brønsted Acids and Bases

In general, molecules such as hydrogen chloride that behave as Brønsted acids are polar, and the hydrogen that is acidic (transferable as a proton) is at the positive end of the

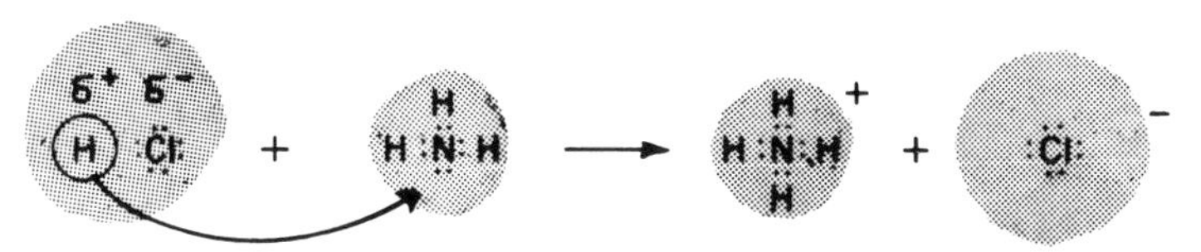

Fig. 3.2. Reaction of HCl and NH_3 Molecules.

dipole. In other words, the bonding electron pair is withdrawn from the hydrogen toward the atom or group (of atoms) to which the hydrogen is attached:

$$\overset{\delta^+}{H} \quad \overset{\delta^-}{:A}$$

In cations that contain hydrogen atoms, these hydrogen atoms are in an electron-poor or *positive* environment, because the total ionic unit within which they are contained is electron-deficient or positive. Hence the hydrogen atoms in cations tend to be transferred as protons, and all hydrogen-containing cations have acidic tendencies.

To be a Brønsted base or proton acceptor, a molecule or ion must have at least one unshared electron pair. If the base is to have appreciable proton-acceptor tendencies, this unshared pair must be located on an atom in a *negative* environment, either in an anion or at the negative end of a dipole. For a base it's a case of "Have pair, will share." (Fig. 3.1). If the base is to be strong, this unshared electron pair must not be held too tightly by the atom on which it is located, because of the inherent electronegativity either of the atom, itself, or of the atoms to which it is attached. The strongest type of base, then, would be an anion with a large negative charge on an atom of low electronegativity.

Relationship of Acidity and Basicity to Charge

From the discussion thus far, we should conclude that, other things being equal, *acidity should increase with positive charge and basicity with negative charge.* And this is true. But it is difficult to keep other things constant. $Fe(H_2O)_6^{+++}$ is indeed a stronger acid than $Fe(H_2O)_6^{++}$, and $Ni(OH)_4^{=}$ a stronger base than $Ni(OH)_4^{-}$.

The spirit, if not the letter, of the rule can be illustrated by the water sequence of acids and bases shown in Fig. 3.3.

H_4O^{++}, if it does indeed exist, is bound to be a powerful acid. Oxide ion, on the other hand, is a potent base, as evi-

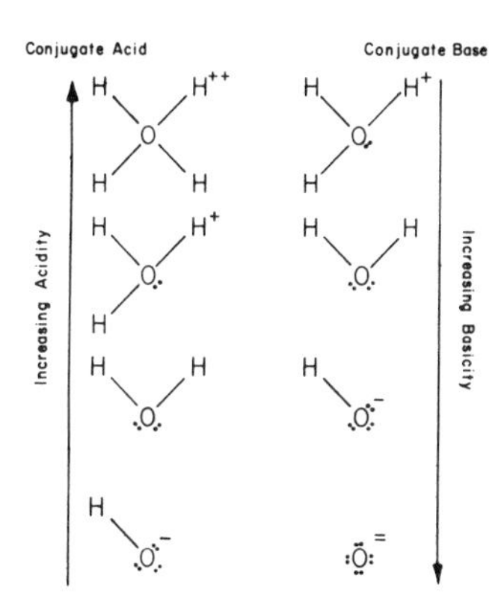

Fig. 3.3. Water Sequence of Acids and Bases.

denced by the familiar conversion of ionic (basic) oxides to hydroxides in water:

$$\underset{\text{Acid}_1}{H\!:\!\ddot{O}\!:\!H} + \underset{\text{Base}_2}{:\!\ddot{O}\!:^{=}} \rightleftharpoons \underset{\text{Acid}_2}{H\!:\!\ddot{O}\!:^{-}} + \underset{\text{Base}_1}{H\!:\!\ddot{O}\!:^{-}}$$

From the fact that this reaction proceeds essentially to completion to the right, it is safe to conclude that oxide ion is a considerably stronger base than hydroxide ion.

Actually, the entire sequence serves to emphasize the obvious—that an acid is a stronger acid than its conjugate base and that a base is a stronger base than its conjugate acid. Thus $H_2PO_4^-$, dihydrogen phosphate ion, is a stronger acid than $HPO_4^{=}$, hydrogen phosphate ion, and a stronger base than H_3PO_4, phosphoric acid.

Acidity, Basicity, and Relative Electronegativities

If we think of an acid, in unit particle terms, as a molecule or an ion containing a positively charged hydrogen, we might expect that the more positive the hydrogen, the stronger the acid. On that basis, we would predict that for any acid HA, the more strongly A withdraws the bonding electron pair from H, the more acid HA would be, i.e., the acidity of HA should increase with the electronegativity of the atom or group A.

When applied within proper limits, this idea will give us valuable mileage. In general, the electronegativity of an atom increases with increasing nuclear charge and with decreasing atomic radius. Hence the relative electronegativity in a horizontal period of elements in the periodic table increases with atomic number. In the first horizontal period of eight (excluding the inert gas neon), for example, the relative electronegativity increases in the order

$$\xrightarrow{\text{Order of increasing electronegativity}}$$
$$\text{Li} < \text{Be} < \text{B} < \text{C} < \text{N} < \text{O} < \text{F}$$

We should predict, therefore, that the acidities of the hydrides should vary in the order

$$\xrightarrow{\text{Order of increasing acidity}}$$
$$\text{LiH} < \text{BeH}_2 < \text{CH}_4 < \text{NH}_3 < \text{H}_2\text{O} < \text{HF}\ ^*$$

As an active metal, lithium has both a strong tendency to give up its single 2*s* valence electron and also an extremely low electronegativity. As a result, not only is lithium hydride devoid of acid properties, but it is actually a salt whose anion is the powerful base $H:^-$, hydride ion. In hydride ion, the electron-rich hydrogen shares its pair of electrons with even weakly acid hydrogen atoms, such as those in water or ethyl alcohol, to form its feeble conjugate acid, molecular hydrogen:

$$\begin{array}{ccccccc} \text{Acid}_1 & + & \text{Base}_2 & \rightarrow & \text{Acid}_2 & + & \text{Base}_1 \\ H_2O & + & H:^- & \rightarrow & H:H & + & OH^- \\ C_2H_5OH & + & H:^- & \rightarrow & H:H & + & C_2H_5O^- \end{array}$$

*Simple BH_3 is unknown. (?)

Beryllium hydride is also basic, though less so than lithium hydride.

Methane, CH_4, has no unshared electron pair, and therefore cannot be a base, but it is a very feeble acid. Ammonia, though a weak acid, is considerably stronger than methane; water is a stronger acid than ammonia, and hydrogen fluoride definitely stronger than water. These experimentally observed relationships, summarized in Fig. 3.4, are exactly those predicted from relative electronegativities.

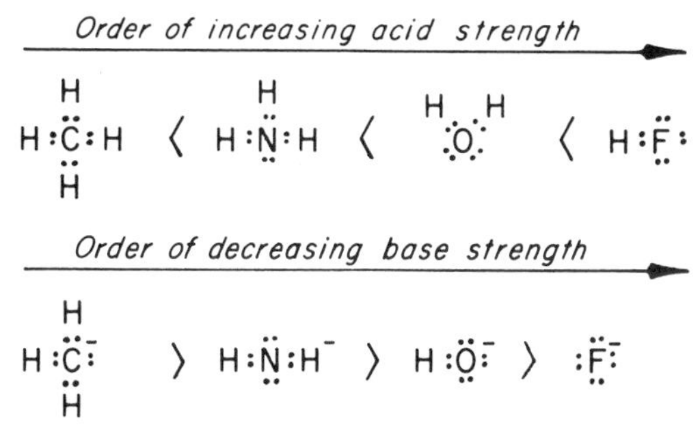

Fig. 3.4. Increase of Acidity with Increasing Electronegativity in the CH_4, NH_3, H_2O, HF Series.

Considering ammonia, water, and hydrogen fluoride now as bases, we should expect that the hetero atoms would exert an increasing strong pull on their valence electrons as the nuclear charge increases. In other words the electrons should be held increasingly tightly in the order $N < O < F$. Conversely, an unshared electron pair, in each case, would be most readily shared by nitrogen, then by oxygen, and least readily by fluorine. In other words we should expect the basicity to increase with decreasing electronegativity of the hetero atoms, and we should predict the orders shown in Fig. 3.5. Again, these correspond to the experimental facts.

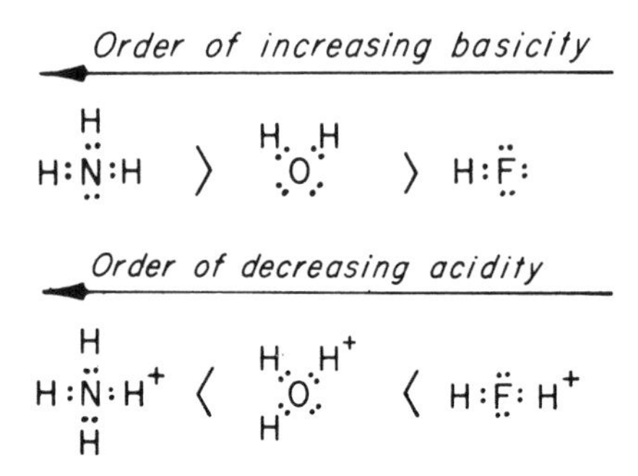

Fig. 3.5. Increase of Basicity with Decreasing Electronegativity in the HF, H_2O, NH_3 Series.

Many of the acids and bases of interest to chemists are compounds in which the basic center is an oxygen or nitrogen atom and the acid hydrogen is one attached to the oxygen or nitrogen. In making generalizations, we shall find it extremely helpful to consider such acids and bases as derivatives of water or ammonia in which one (or more) of the hydrogen atoms has been replaced by another atom or group.

Each of the parent compounds water and ammonia has its own characteristic acid and base strengths. The electronegativity of hydrogen is approximately the same as that of carbon, much higher than that of active metals such as sodium and potassium, but considerably lower than that of active non-metals such as oxygen and chlorine.

Now, for any derivative of water or ammonia, YOH or YNH_2, the acid and base strengths can vary widely in either direction from those of the parent compounds, depending upon the electronegativity of Y.

If Y is more electronegative than hydrogen—

then Y will decrease the *electron density* or *electron pair availability* at an oxygen or nitrogen atom and will *increase electron pair withdrawal* from the hydrogen linked to the oxygen or nitrogen atom. This means that the compound YOH or YNH_2 will be *less basic* and *more acidic* than its parent compound.*

If Y is less electronegative than hydrogen—

then Y will *increase* the *electron density* or *electron pair availability* at the oxygen or nitrogen atom and will *decrease electron pair withdrawal* from the hydrogen bonded to the oxygen or nitrogen atom. As a result, YOH or YNH_2 will be *more basic* and *less acidic* than its parent compound.

Relative Acidities and Basicities of Water Derivatives

Let's look first at the derivatives of water, YOH, in which one of the hydrogen atoms of water has been replaced by an atom or group of atoms Y. Compounds of this type vary from such ionic hydroxides as potassium hydroxide, KOH, and sodium hydroxide, to such powerful acids as sulfuric acid $SO_2(OH)_2$ and perchloric acid, ClO_3OH.

Before we consider these formulas, let's take a closer look at the electronic structure of the water molecule itself.

Oxygen is much more electronegative than hydrogen, and, on the average, the electron pairs shared between the oxygen atom and the hydrogen atoms in the water molecule are displaced away from the hydrogens toward the oxygen. The angle between the two H—O bonds is 105°. Since the two bonds are polar and the molecule is unsymmetrical, the water molecule as a whole is polar, with the hydrogens at the positive end of the dipole and the oxygen at the negative end, as shown diagrammatically in Fig. 3.6.

This picture of the water molecule points up its amphiprotic nature. The hydrogen atoms are in a somewhat electron-deficient or positive environment and are, therefore, somewhat acidic. The oxygen atom, with its unshared

*In fact, highly electronegative atoms or groups are often described as atoms or groups which *increase* the *acidity* and *decrease* the *basicity* of molecules into which they are introduced.

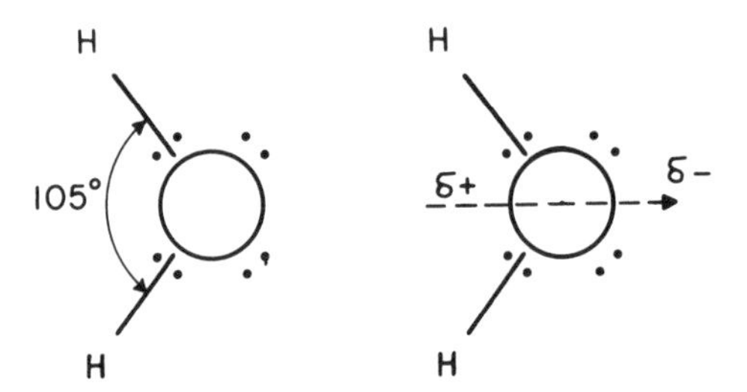

Fig. 3.6. Polar Nature of the Water Molecule.

electron pairs and its negative environment, is a somewhat basic center.

The effect of the relative electronegativity of an atom on group Y, when substituted for a hydrogen atom, on the acidity of the hydrogen and the basicity of the oxygen is shown schematically in Fig. 3.7.

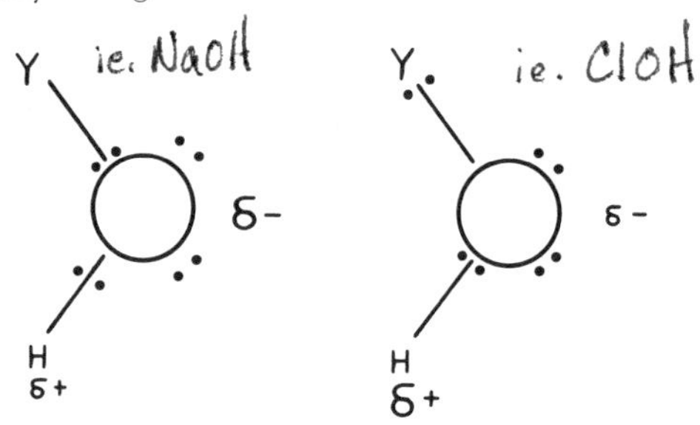

Fig. 3.7. Effect of the Electronegativity of Y in YOH on the Electron Density at H and O.

If Y is sodium, which as an active metal has an extremely low electronegativity, the electron pair is released completely to the oxygen with the formation of sodium and hydroxide ions:

$$Na^{+} \;\Big|\; {}^{-}\!:\ddot{\underset{\cdot\cdot}{O}}:H$$

This is, of course, the extreme situation in which the oxygen, as part of a negative ion, becomes a highly basic center, and the hydrogen, as part of an anion, loses almost all of its acidity. We should expect YOH to be ionic whenever Y is a metal with a very small attraction for electrons—in general, an active metal of low ionization potential.

But if Y is chlorine, the highly electronegative chlorine atom will decrease the electron density at the oxygen atom and will increase the effective electronegativity of the oxygen atom in withdrawing the electrons from the hydrogen.* This fact is represented schematically in Fig. 3.8.

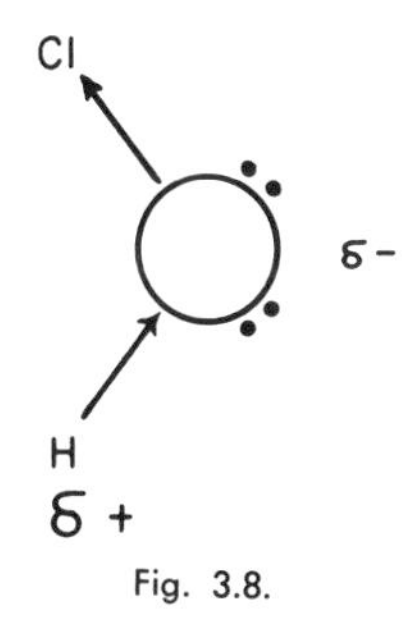

Fig. 3.8.

As a result, hypochlorous acid is a considerably weaker base and stronger acid than water.

All shades of intermediate acid and base strengths between those of hydroxide ion, on the one hand, and hypochlorous acid, on the other, are observed in compounds YOH, where the electronegativity of atom Y is greater than that of sodium but less than that of chlorine. In general, however, we may say that the hydroxides of metals are basic, whereas the hydroxyl compounds of non-metals are acids.

As another example of the effect of an increase in the relative electronegativity of Y in increasing acidity and decreasing

*Another way of expressing this idea is to say that the group ClO is more electronegative than HO.

basicity in YOH, consider a series of compounds in which all the central atoms to which the OH groups are attached belong to the same family and exhibit the same oxidation state. In any family of elements in the periodic table, relative electronegativity increases with increasing proximity of the valence electrons to the nucleus—in other words, from bottom to top in the periodic table. Hence we should expect the acidity of any family of hydroxyl compounds to decrease and the basicity to increase with increasing atomic number. For the known hypohalous acids and for the halic acids (where Y is a group of atoms, rather than a single atom), we should predict the orders shown in Fig. 3.9.

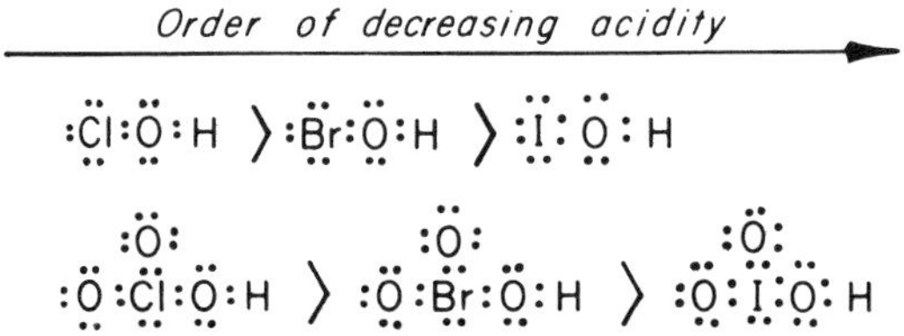

Order of decreasing acidity →

:Cl:O:H > :Br:O:H > :I:O:H

:O:Cl:O:H (with :O: on Cl) > :O:Br:O:H (with :O: on Br) > :O:I:O:H (with :O: on I)

Fig. 3.9. Decrease in Acidity of the Hypohalous and Halic Acids as the Electronegativity of the Halogen Decreases.

Similarly, for the acids of the nitric acid family, we should predict the decrease in acidity with decrease in electronegativity shown in Fig. 3.10.

Order of decreasing acidity →

Nitric Acid	*Phosphoric Acid*	*Arsenic Acid*	*Antimonic Acid*	*Bismuthic Acid*
HNO_3 >	H_3PO_4 >	H_3AsO_4 >	$HSb(OH)_6$ >	$HBiO_3$

Fig. 3.10. Decrease in Acidity with Decrease in Electronegativity of the Central Atom in the Nitric Acid Family.

In all cases, our predictions correspond to experimental facts.

For compounds containing the OH group attached to the same central atom, the acidity increases and the basicity decreases with an increase in the number of electronegative atoms attached to the central atom, i.e., with an increase in the oxidation number of the central atom. The fact is well illustrated by the oxygen acids of chlorine listed in Fig. 3.11.

Order of increasing oxidation number →

Hypochlorous Acid		*Chlorous Acid*		*Chloric Acid*		*Perchloric Acid*
:Cl:O:H	$<$	:O:Cl:O:H	$<$	:O:Cl(:O:):O:H	$<$	:O:Cl(:O:)(:O:):O:H

Fig. 3.11. Increase of Acidity in Oxygen Acids of Chlorine with Increase in Oxidation Number of Chlorine.

The linking of highly electronegative oxygen atoms to chlorine increases the effective electronegativity of the chlorine, so that the electronegativity of the Y groups increases in the order $Cl < OCl < O_2Cl < O_3Cl$.

Now take a look at a series of hydroxyl compounds, YOH, of the elements in a horizontal period in the periodic table, such as the following (written with Y bracketed in each case): [Na]OH, [HOMg]OH, $[(HO)_2Al]OH$, [(HO)OSi]OH, $[(HO)_2OP]OH$, $[(HO)O_2S]OH$, and $[O_3Cl]OH$. Not only does the electronegativity of the central atom here increase with atomic number, but so does the oxidation number. Hence, the electronegativity of the entire group Y increases sharply with atomic number, and you can predict with confidence the increase in acidity and decrease in basicity from sodium hydroxide through perchloric acid in the series shown in Fig. 3.12.

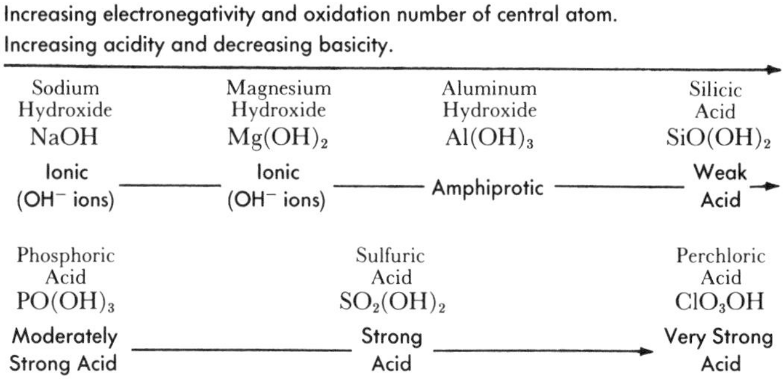

Increasing electronegativity and oxidation number of central atom.
Increasing acidity and decreasing basicity. →

Sodium Hydroxide $NaOH$	Magnesium Hydroxide $Mg(OH)_2$	Aluminum Hydroxide $Al(OH)_3$	Silicic Acid $SiO(OH)_2$
Ionic (OH^- ions) ——	Ionic (OH^- ions) ——	Amphiprotic ——	Weak Acid →

Phosphoric Acid $PO(OH)_3$	Sulfuric Acid $SO_2(OH)_2$	Perchloric Acid ClO_3OH
Moderately Strong Acid ——	Strong Acid →	Very Strong Acid

Fig. 3.12. Increase in Acidity and Decrease in Basicity with Increasing Electronegativity and Oxidation Number of the Central Atom in the NaOH—O_3ClOH Series.

The facts confirm your predictions.

Predictions about Some Ammonia Derivatives

These same principles apply to derivatives of ammonia, YNH_2. However, because ammonia is more basic and less acidic than water, YNH_2 for any given Y is more basic and less acidic than YOH.*

Sodamide, $NaNH_2$ (p. 24), like sodium hydroxide, is ionic, and amide ion is considerably more basic than hydroxide ion.

Chloramine, $ClNH_2$, is considerably less basic and more acidic than ammonia, but is definitely less acidic and more basic than hypochlorous acid.

Nitramine, NO_2NH_2, is much less basic and more acidic than ammonia, but less acidic and more basic than nitric acid.

Hydrazine, NH_2NH_2, as would be expected from the fact that the NH_2 group is more electronegative than hydrogen, is somewhat less basic and more acidic than ammonia. On

*For a thorough comparison of the ammonia and water systems of compounds, see Sisler, H. H., "Chemistry in Non-Aqueous Solvents," Reinhold Publishing Corporation, New York, 1961, p. 26.

the other hand, hydrazine is less acidic and more basic than hydroxylamine, NH_2OH. In keeping with the generalizations concerning the relative acidities and basicities of oxygen versus nitrogen compounds, the more basic center in hydroxylamine is the nitrogen atom, and the more acidic hydrogen is that attached to oxygen.

Relative Acidities of Some Organic Oxygen and Nitrogen Compounds

Organic chemists generally agree that alkyl groups (R groups) such as methyl (CH_3), ethyl (CH_3CH_2), and *n*-propyl ($CH_3CH_2CH_2$) are slightly less electronegative than hydrogen. It is not surprising, therefore, that alcohols are in general somewhat more basic than water, and that primary amines (RNH_2) are somewhat more basic and less acidic than ammonia. The basic ionization constant in water solution, K_b, for ethylamine, $CH_3CH_2NH_2$, for example, is 5.6×10^{-4}, as compared with 1.8×10^{-5} for ammonia:

$$\underset{\text{Acid}_1}{H:\ddot{\underset{\cdot\cdot}{O}}:H} + \underset{\text{Base}_2}{CH_3CH_2\overset{H}{\ddot{\underset{\cdot\cdot}{N}}}:H} \rightleftharpoons \underset{\text{Acid}_2}{CH_3CH_2\overset{H}{\underset{H}{\ddot{\underset{\cdot\cdot}{N}}}}:H^+} + \underset{\text{Base}_1}{:\ddot{\underset{\cdot\cdot}{O}}:H^-}$$

$$K_b = 5.6 \times 10^{-4}$$

An acyl group $\left(R{-}\overset{O}{\overset{\|}{C}}{-}\right)$ is considerably more electronegative than hydrogen, and we would expect amides $\left(R{-}\overset{O}{\overset{\|}{C}}{-}NH_2\right)$ to be weaker bases and stronger acids than ammonia, just as carboxylic acids $\left(R{-}\overset{O}{\overset{\|}{C}}{-}OH\right)$ are stronger acids and weaker bases than water. Simple amides are weaker acids than carboxylic acids; in fact, they are weaker acids than water. With the introduction of a second acyl group to form an imide

$\left(R{-}\overset{\displaystyle O}{\overset{\|}{C}}{-}\overset{\displaystyle H}{\overset{|}{N}}{-}\overset{\displaystyle O}{\overset{\|}{C}}{-}R\right)$, however, the acidity of the hydrogen on the nitrogen is increased above that of hydrogen in water. In experimental terms, this means that even water insoluble imides dissolve in dilute solutions of sodium hydroxide.

Relative Acidities of Some Methane Derivatives

With no unshared electron pairs, methane and other alkanes such as ethane (CH_3CH_3) and propane ($CH_3CH_2CH_3$) cannot act as Brønsted bases. All are, however, feeble acids, and the same generalizations may be made about the relative acidities of derivatives of methane (YCH_3), and of other alkanes, that were discussed for derivatives of water and ammonia.

Methane is so weak an acid that sodium methide, $NaCH_3$, is difficult to prepare, and methide ion $\left(H : \overset{\displaystyle H}{\underset{\displaystyle H}{\ddot{\underset{..}{C}}}} :^{-}\right)$ is a powerful base. Chloromethane $\left(: \ddot{\underset{..}{Cl}} : \overset{\displaystyle H}{\underset{\displaystyle H}{\ddot{\underset{..}{C}}}} : H\right)$ is more acidic than methane, but certainly not comparable in acidity to hypochlorous acid or chloramine. Trichloromethane, or chloroform $\left(: \ddot{\underset{..}{Cl}} : \overset{: \ddot{\underset{..}{Cl}} :}{\underset{: \ddot{\underset{..}{Cl}} :}{\ddot{\underset{..}{C}}}} : H\right)$, is considerably more acidic than chloromethane.

Substitution in the methane molecule of an acyl group for the less electronegative hydrogen atom gives a methyl ketone $\left(R{-}\overset{\displaystyle O}{\overset{\|}{C}}{-}CH_3\right)$. Such a compound is considerably more acidic than methane, though still less so than water. With the introduction of a second acyl group, the acidity of the hydrogen attached to the central carbon is increased above that of water.

From an experimental standpoint, then, diketones of the type

$$R-\overset{\overset{O}{\|}}{C}-\underset{\underset{H}{|}}{\overset{\overset{H}{|}}{C}}-\overset{\overset{O}{\|}}{C}-R$$

are soluble in dilute sodium hydroxide.

The substitution of highly electronegative atoms for hydrogen in a somewhat more remote site in the molecule can still increase the acidity of hydrogen. For example, the effective electronegativity of acetyl groups $\left(CH_3-\overset{\overset{O}{\|}}{C}-\right)$ increases sharply as chlorine atoms are substituted for hydrogen. Thus, we have the following order of increasing electronegativity:

$$CH_3-\overset{\overset{O}{\|}}{C}- < ClCH_2-\overset{\overset{O}{\|}}{C}- < Cl_2CH-\overset{\overset{O}{\|}}{C}- < Cl_3C-\overset{\overset{O}{\|}}{C}-$$

Experimentally we observe that chloroacetic acid $\left(ClCH_2-\overset{\overset{O}{\|}}{C}-OH\right)$, with $K_a = 1.6 \times 10^{-4}$, is considerably stronger than acetic acid ($K_a = 1.8 \times 10^{-5}$), and that trichloroacetic acid $\left(Cl_3C-\overset{\overset{O}{\|}}{C}-OH\right)$ is comparable in acid strength to sulfuric and nitric acids.

The effect diminishes rapidly, however, as it is relayed through a carbon chain. For example, the acid ionization constants at 25° C for α-chlorobutyric $\left(CH_3CH_2CHCl-\overset{\overset{O}{\|}}{C}-OH\right)$, β-chlorobutyric $\left(CH_3CHClCH_2-\overset{\overset{O}{\|}}{C}-OH\right)$, and γ-chlorobutyric $\left(ClCH_2CH_2CH_2-\overset{\overset{O}{\|}}{C}-OH\right)$ acids are 1.5×10^{-3}, 8.8×10^{-5}, and 1.5×10^{-5} (the same as that for butyric acid itself), respectively.

The Hydrogen Halide Problem

Applied within proper limits, the generalization that in any series of compounds, HA, the acidity of H increases with the electronegativity of A is most useful. We have just seen that this rule is valid for any series of acids in which H is attached, in every case, to the same element or to elements in the same horizontal period. But electronegativity is not the whole story.

Fluorine, at the extreme right and top of the periodic table (excluding the inert gases), is the most electronegative element in the periodic table. But hydrogen fluoride is certainly not the strongest acid of the simple hydrides. In fact, acidity of the hydrogen halides increases rapidly in the sequence

$$HF \ll HCl < HBr < HI,$$

exactly the reverse of that predicted solely on the basis of electronegativity.

The anomaly, is of course, not peculiar to the hydrogen halides, for acidity in the water family of hydrides increases in the order

$$H_2O < H_2S < H_2Se < H_2Te$$

and in the ammonia family $NH_3 < PH_3 < AsH_3 < SbH_3$. In each case, the acidity order is the reverse of the electronegativity order.

These anomalies arise because the electronegativity principle of acidity is actually an oversimplification. It is concerned only with the structure of the acid itself. But the structure of the conjugate base is also important in determining the acidity of any acid. In fact, it is not the nature of the acid alone, nor the nature of the base alone, but rather the free energy relationship between the conjugate base and acid that determines the acidity of the acid. In other words, *for any acid*

HA, the more stable A^- is as compared with HA, the stronger HA is as an acid. A strong acid, then, is one whose conjugate base is relatively stable compared to the acid itself. Any factor that stabilizes the anion more than it stabilizes the acid should increase acidity; any factor that stabilizes the acid more than it stabilizes the anion should decrease acidity.

Usually, the base-acid relative stability viewpoint of acid strength leads to the same predictions as does the relative electronegativity viewpoint. For in general, the more strongly the atom on group A withdraws electrons from H in HA (the greater the electronegativity of A), the more stable is A^-, and the greater is the tendency of HA to go to the anionic form A^-. This is logical, because the more strongly A tends to be the negative end of the dipole in HA,

$$\overset{\delta^+}{H} : \overset{\delta^-}{A}$$

the more easily A should be able to accommodate the pair of electrons left behind when H^+ leaves, i.e., the more stable the ion $A:^-$ should be. Thus, for the series, CH_4, NH_3, H_2O, and HF, the relative stability of the anions would be expected to increase markedly with increasing electronegativity of the central ion, as indeed it does:

Order of Increasing Stability of Anions →

$$H:\underset{H}{\overset{H}{\ddot{\underset{\cdot\cdot}{C}}}}:^- < :\underset{H}{\overset{H}{\ddot{\underset{\cdot\cdot}{N}}}}:^- < H:\ddot{\underset{\cdot\cdot}{O}}:^- < :\ddot{\underset{\cdot\cdot}{F}}:^-$$

In fact, the stability of the halide ions also increases with increasing electronegativity in the expected order:

Increasing Stability of Halide Ions →

$$:\ddot{\underset{\cdot\cdot}{I}}:^- < :\ddot{\underset{\cdot\cdot}{Br}}:^- < :\ddot{\underset{\cdot\cdot}{Cl}}:^- < :\ddot{\underset{\cdot\cdot}{F}}:^-$$

But, as the electronegativity of the halogen atom increases, so also does the strength of the HA bond,* and therefore the stability of HA:

$$\xrightarrow{\text{Increasing Stability of Hydrogen Halides}}$$

$$HI < HBr < HCl < HF$$

This, too, is expected. But the real anomaly in the case of the hydrogen halides is that somehow *the increase in the stability of the halide ions does not keep pace with the increase in the stability of the hydrogen halides* themselves. In other words, for the hydrogen halides, HA, (and the water and ammonia families, as well), the combined effect of an increase in the electronegativity and a decrease in the size of A is to stabilize the undissociated acid HA more than the anion A^-. The over-all result, therefore, is that there is a *decrease* of the stability of the halide ion A^- compared to its conjugate acid HA in the sequence $HI > HBr > HCl > HF$. This is, therefore, the order of *decreasing* acidity.

Acidity, Basicity, and Ion Size

These facts certainly suggest that the stability of an anion A^- is dependent upon other factors in addition to the electronegativity of A. Certainly this is the case. A number of complex factors are involved. Some of them, such as the solvation of the anion, are rather indeterminate. In the special case of hydrogen fluoride the complexing of fluoride ions with undissociated hydrogen fluoride molecules to form ions of the type HF_2^- is undoubtedly important. But there is one simple and clear-cut factor which we should expect to be especially significant in all cases—the size of the anion, or, more specifically, the extent to which the negative charge can be distributed or diffused in the anion.

*One of the standard methods for the calculation of relative electronegativities of various elements is based on the relative bond strengths of the bonds in the hydrides of the elements.

According to the laws of physics, the stability of any charged system is increased by dispersal of the charge. We have already seen (p. 8) that bare proton, with its tremendously high ratio of charge to size, is unstable. With the addition of a water molecule to form the much larger hydronium ion, the charge is effectively dispersed, and a much more stable ion results. Dispersal or smearing of charge in an ion over a larger volume tends to stabilize the ion.

In the halide ions, the negative charge is spread or dispersed over the entire ion. The larger the ion, the more effectively the negative charge is spread or diffused, and the lower is the charge density at any given point in the ion. Definitely, then, we would expect the sharp increase in ion size in the sequence

$$:\ddot{\underset{\cdot\cdot}{\mathrm{F}}}:^- < :\ddot{\underset{\cdot\cdot}{\mathrm{Cl}}}:^- < :\ddot{\underset{\cdot\cdot}{\mathrm{Br}}}:^- < :\ddot{\underset{\cdot\cdot}{\mathrm{I}}}:^-$$

to serve as a stabilizing factor for the ions in the same order. We see then, that in this series increasing size of the ion works in exactly the opposite direction from increasing electronegativity in favoring increased ion stabilization.

Similarly, for the hydrides of the water and ammonia series, it is the size of the central atom which determines almost completely the extent to which the negative charge in the conjugate base can be dispersed or diffused. Once more, we would expect increased ion size to favor increased ion stability in the order

$$\mathrm{H}:\ddot{\underset{\cdot\cdot}{\mathrm{O}}}:^- < \mathrm{H}:\ddot{\underset{\cdot\cdot}{\mathrm{S}}}:^- < \mathrm{H}:\ddot{\underset{\cdot\cdot}{\mathrm{Se}}}:^- < \mathrm{H}:\ddot{\underset{\cdot\cdot}{\mathrm{Te}}}:^-$$

$$\mathrm{H}:\ddot{\underset{\cdot\cdot}{\mathrm{N}}}:\mathrm{H}^- < \mathrm{H}:\ddot{\underset{\cdot\cdot}{\mathrm{P}}}:\mathrm{H}^- < \mathrm{H}:\ddot{\underset{\cdot\cdot}{\mathrm{As}}}:\mathrm{H}^- < \mathrm{H}:\ddot{\underset{\cdot\cdot}{\mathrm{Sb}}}:\mathrm{H}^-$$

Again, the effect of an increase in the size of the central atom in promoting ion stability runs counter to the effect of increasing electronegativity. The total result is that, in each of these three series of hydrides, as the size of the central atom decreases, the stability of the anion, A^-, increases less rapidly than that of the acid, HA, itself. The observed result is that the acidity of acids in any one of the families decreases from bottom to top in the periodic table. These conclusions are summarized for the hydrogen halides in Fig. 3.13.

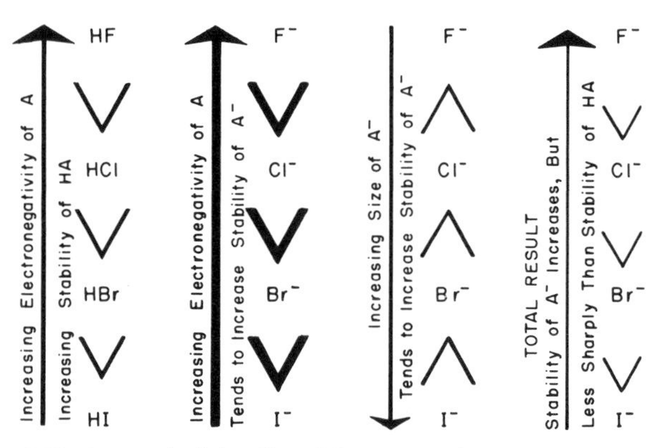

Fig. 3.13. As a result of the effect of the opposing factors (electronegativity of A and size of A^-) on the stability of A^-, stability of A^- increases from bottom to top *less* sharply than stability of HA. Observed result—acidity of HA decreases from bottom to top.

General Applicability of Charge Dispersal Principle

The principle that ion stability increases with charge dispersal has wide applicability. For a series of compounds containing the OH group attached to the same central atom (see p. 45), the acidity increases with an increase in the oxidation number of the central atom (with the number of electronegative atoms such as oxygen or fluorine linked to the central atom). Undoubtedly this is due in large part to increasing stabilization (through charge dispersal) of the conjugate base as the number of oxygen or fluorine atoms attached to the central atom increases.

Consider, for example, the increase in charge dispersal in

$$:\ddot{\underset{..}{Cl}}:\ddot{\underset{..}{O}}:^- < :\ddot{\underset{..}{O}}:\ddot{\underset{..}{Cl}}:\ddot{\underset{..}{O}}:^- < :\ddot{\underset{..}{O}}:\overset{:\ddot{O}:}{\underset{..}{\ddot{Cl}}}:\ddot{\underset{..}{O}}:^- < :\ddot{\underset{..}{O}}:\overset{:\ddot{O}:}{\underset{:\underset{..}{O}:}{\ddot{Cl}}}:\ddot{\underset{..}{O}}:^-$$

Increase in charge dispersal increases the stability of the ion and therefore the acidity of its conjugate acid.

Likewise, a comparison of charge dispersals in F^- and $HSiF_6^-$ ions

$$:\ddot{\underset{..}{F}}:^- \qquad\qquad \left[H:\ddot{\underset{..}{F}}:\overset{\ddot{F}\ \ \ddot{F}}{\underset{\underset{..}{F}\ \ \underset{..}{F}}{Si}}:\ddot{\underset{..}{F}}:\right]^-$$

certainly suggests why fluosilicic acid (H_2SiF_6) is a much stronger acid than hydrogen fluoride.

Resonance and Acidity and Basicity

Often the charge on an ion, either anion or cation, is effectively dispersed as a result of *resonance.* In such cases, *resonance* may have a pronounced influence on acidities or basicities. Here is the story.

Frequently, for a particular molecule, ion, or free radical we can write two or more reasonable electronic formulas which differ only in the distribution of certain of the electrons. According to the concept of *resonance,* the true structure of the molecule, ion, or radical is then not that represented by any one of the individual electronic formulas, but is, rather, an intermediate structure which cannot be represented by a single electronic formula. The substance involved is then said to be a *resonance hybrid** receiving contributions from the

*For example, sulfur dioxide is a resonance hybrid which receives contributions from the resonance structures $:\ddot{O}\!\!\overset{\ddot{S}}{\ }\!\!:\ddot{O}:$ and $:\ddot{O}:\overset{\ddot{S}}{\ }\ddot{O}:$

various hypothetical *resonance structures* represented by the different electronic formulas, and the phenomenon is called resonance.† The properties of the substance are, in general, a summation of those expected for the various hypothetical structures, with one extremely important added effect—the substance itself is always more stable than would be predicted for even the most stable of the various hypothetical structures. The added stability conferred upon the substance through resonance is called "resonance stabilization."

Let's apply these ideas at once to a familiar case. Acetic acid ($CH_3—\overset{\overset{\displaystyle O}{\|}}{C}—OH$) is a stronger acid than water. We have said (p. 49) that the $R—\overset{\overset{\displaystyle O}{\|}}{C}—$ group is more electronegative than hydrogen and that substitution of an $R—\overset{\overset{\displaystyle O}{\|}}{C}—$ group for a hydrogen atom in the water molecule increases the acidity of the remaining hydrogen. But now, from our new viewpoint, consider the structure of the acetate ion. We can write for it two different reasonable electronic formulas, (1) and (2), representing two equivalent but different resonance structures (indicated by doubleheaded arrow) or a composite structure, (3):

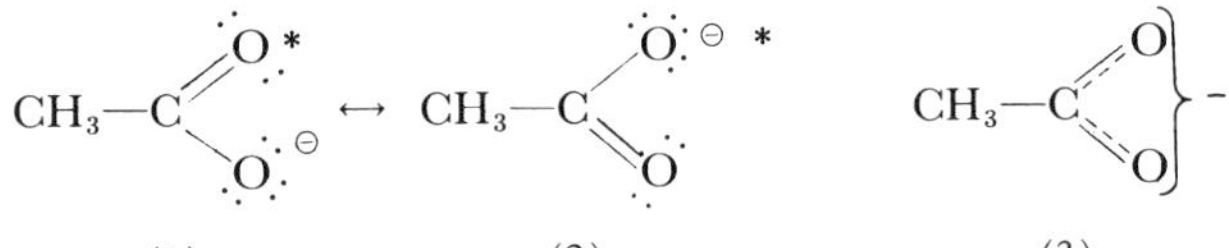

$$CH_3—C\begin{matrix}\nearrow\!\!\!\!\!= \ddot{O}:{}^{*} \\ \searrow :\ddot{O}:^{\ominus}\end{matrix} \leftrightarrow CH_3—C\begin{matrix}\nearrow :\ddot{O}:^{\ominus}\ {}^{*} \\ \searrow\!\!\!\!\!= \ddot{O}:\end{matrix} \qquad CH_3—C\left.\begin{matrix}\cdots O \\ \cdots O\end{matrix}\right\}^{-}$$

(1) (2) (3)

†The term is an unfortunate one because it implies an oscillation or dynamic equilibrium. This is *definitely not what is meant.*

*We shall follow the practice of encircling a unit positive or negative charge whenever an attempt is made to localize the charge on a particular atom in an electronic formula.

The true structure of acetate ion is neither that represented by formula (1) nor that represented by formula (2), but something intermediate which cannot be represented by a single classical electronic formula. Actually, acetate ion is more stable than either formula (1) or (2), alone, would indicate. And this can be explained readily on the basis that in acetate ion the negative charge is not localized on either of the two oxygen atoms alone, but is actually shared equally between the two. The high degree of resonance stabilization conferred upon the acetate ion as a result of this charge dispersal is considerably greater than the resonance stabilization in the conjugate acid, acetic acid (see p. 95), and resonance therefore serves to make acetic acid a stronger acid than water. The same considerations apply to formic acid $\left(H\text{—}\overset{\overset{\displaystyle O}{\|}}{C}\text{—}OH\right)$ and other carboxylic acids $\left(R\text{—}\overset{\overset{\displaystyle O}{\|}}{C}\text{—}OH\right)$. Electron withdrawing groups, W (Fig. 3.14a), such as Cl_3C— (see p. 49), disperse the negative charge still further, stabilize the anion, and increase acidity. Electron releasing groups, R (Fig. 3.14b), intensify the negative charge, destabilize the anion, and decrease acidity.

Let's look at a few other interesting examples, from among the thousands that might well be cited. Acetylacetone $\left(CH_3\text{—}\overset{\overset{\displaystyle O}{\|}}{C}\text{—}CH_2\text{—}\overset{\overset{\displaystyle O}{\|}}{C}\text{—}CH_3\right)$, (p. 49), is a much stronger acid than methane, of which it may be considered a derivative, because

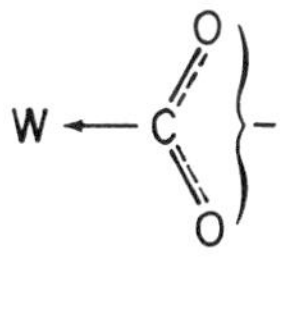

Fig. 3.14a. W withdraws electrons, disperses negative charge, stabilizes ion, strengthens acid.

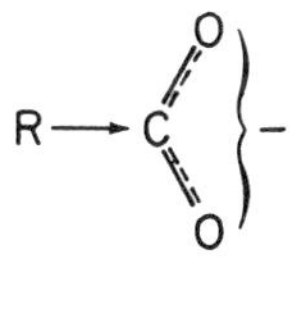

Fig. 3.14b. R releases electrons, intensifies negative charge, destablizes ion, weakens acid.

the negative charge in its conjugate base is shared by a carbon and two oxygen atoms, and resonance stabilization of the ion is considerably greater than that of the acid:

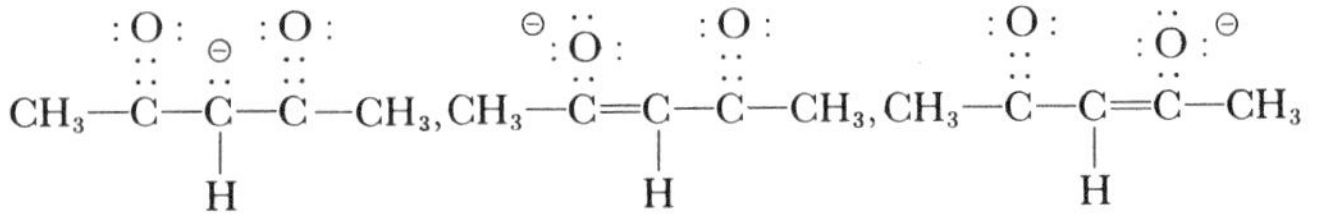

$$CH_3-\overset{\overset{:\ddot{O}:}{\|}}{C}-\underset{H}{\overset{\ominus}{C}}-\overset{\overset{:\ddot{O}:}{\|}}{C}-CH_3, \quad CH_3-\overset{\overset{\ominus:\ddot{O}:}{|}}{C}=\underset{H}{C}-\overset{\overset{:\ddot{O}:}{\|}}{C}-CH_3, \quad CH_3-\overset{\overset{:\ddot{O}:}{\|}}{C}-\underset{H}{C}=\overset{\overset{:\ddot{O}:\ominus}{|}}{C}-CH_3$$

Similarly, phenol is a stronger acid than water, (p. 19), because the negative charge on the oxygen is shared, to some extent, over three carbon atoms in the benzene ring:*

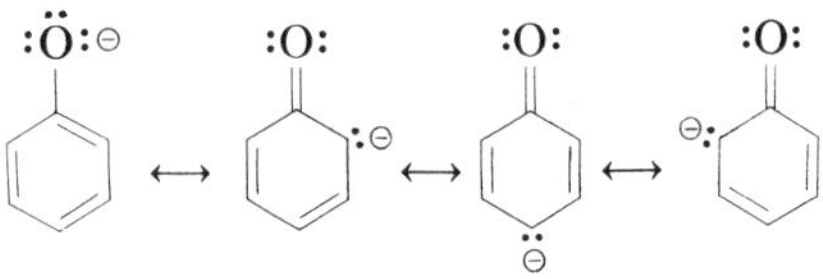

:Ö:⊖ (phenoxide ring) ⟷ :O: (ring, ⊖ ortho) ⟷ :O: (ring, ⊖ para) ⟷ :O: (ring, ⊖ ortho)

In the same way, charge dispersal in a cation serves to increase the stability of the cation, and, therefore, the basicity of its conjugate base. For example, guanidine $\left(NH_2-\overset{\overset{NH}{\|}}{C}-NH_2\right)$ is a strong base, much stronger than ammonia, because the positive charge in its conjugate acid, guanidinium ion $\left(NH_2-\overset{\overset{\oplus NH_2}{\|}}{C}-NH_2\right)$ is dispersed equally over the entire ion through resonance (try writing the additional resonance structures yourself).

The charge dispersal principle can also be used to determine the most acidic (or most basic) of alternative potential acid (or base) sites. For example, which of the three types of hydrogen in propionaldehyde $CH_3CH_2-\overset{\overset{O}{\|}}{C}-H$ is most acidic?

*Each corner of the hexagon represents CH.

The answer is: the hydrogen at the central carbon, because removal of proton at that point leads to an anion whose negative charge is shared by the oxygen:

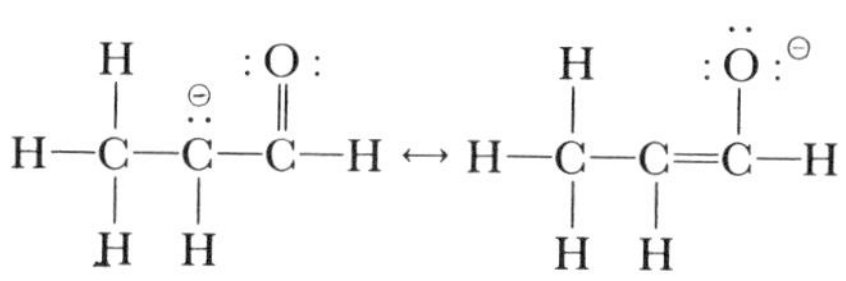

```
                                            ..
     H      :O:              H         :O:⊖
     |   ⊖   ‖               |          |
     |   ..  ‖               |          |
H—C—C—C—H  ↔  H—C—C=C—H
     |    |                  |    |
     H   H                   H   H
```

Similarly, we can predict the structure for the conjugate acid (p. 28) of acetic acid. It is $CH_3—C(OH)_2^+$, because in this ion the positive charge can be shared by both oxygens and the carboxyl carbon:

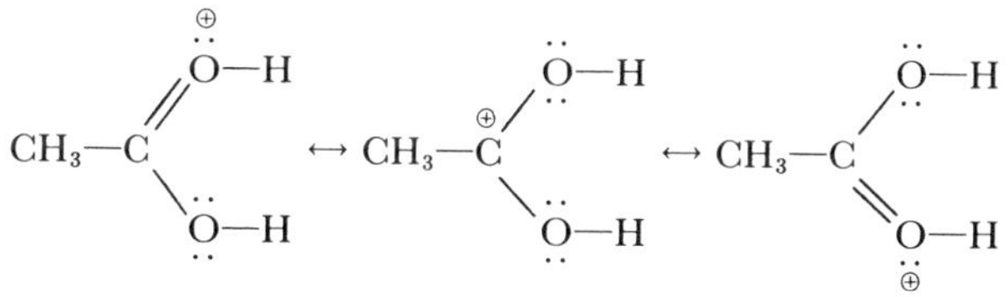

```
          ⊕
          ..                    ..                      ..
          O—H                   O—H                     O—H
        //                 ⊕  / ..                    / ..
CH3—C           ↔  CH3—C             ↔  CH3—C
        \                      \                      \\
          ..                    ..
          O—H                   O—H                     O—H
          ..                    ..                      ..
                                                        ⊕
```

Catalysis by strong protonic acids of many of the characteristic reactions of acetic acid is attributable to the formation of this ion (see p. 98).

chapter four

THE LEWIS CONCEPT OF ACIDITY AND BASICITY

(or, The Electron Shell Game)

By paraphrasing Brønsted slightly, we can set up the following definitions for Brønsted acids and bases:

Acid—*any species containing hydrogen which (as a proton) can accept a share in a pair of electrons.*

Base—*any species which can share an electron pair with a proton.*

Now, inspect these definitions from the standpoint of their conceptual breadth. One word in each definition severely limits and restricts them. The words are "hydrogen" and "proton." You might ask, "Why limit electron-pair-sharing to proton? What's so special about hydrogen, anyhow?"

Or, more elegantly, you might quote the versatile chemist G. N. Lewis (1875–1946), for many years an outstanding professor of chemistry at the University of California at Berkeley. Lewis maintained that "any instructive extension of the idea of acids has been prevented by what I am tempted to call the cult of the proton."

The Lewis Concept as an Extension of the Brønsted Concept

The logical conceptual extensions of the Brønsted definitions suggest themselves automatically:

Acid—*any species containing any atom which can accept a share in an electron pair.*

Base—*any species which can share an electron pair with any electron-pair acceptor.*

Or, as Lewis proposed:

An acid is an electron-pair acceptor.
A base is an electron-pair donor.
An acid-base reaction is the sharing of an electron pair with an acid by a base.

These three simple definitions constitute the heart of what is now known as the Lewis concept of acids and bases. Experimentally and conceptually, they are an extension of the Brønsted definitions. In one broad sweep, they unleash the concept from its dependence upon hydrogen and open a broad new vista of acid-base chemistry.

The Fundamental Lewis Acid-Base Reaction

The fundamental acid-base reaction in the Lewis sense is the formation of a coordinate covalent bond between an acid and a base. The base is the electron-pair donor, the acid the acceptor. The process is called *neutralization*, or simply coordination. The product is a *coordinated compound*, *coordinated complex*, or *adduct*, made up of an acid portion and a base portion. A typical, and oft-cited example is the reaction of the acid boron trifluoride with the base ammonia to form the *coordinated complex* or *adduct* BF_3NH_3:

```
Acid  +   Base  ————→Coordinated Complex
  F        H                F  H
  ..       ..               .. ..
F:B  +  :N:H  ———→       F:B:N:H
  ..       ..               .. ..
  F        H                F  H
```

The coordinated molecule may be thought of as being made up of the acid portion BF_3 and the base portion NH_3.

Classification of Lewis Acids

Bases in the Lewis system are essentially the same as those in the Brønsted system, because molecules or ions which share a pair of electrons with any other electron-pair acceptors, or Lewis acids, as a rule do so also with proton.

The range of acids, however, is greatly extended by the Lewis concept; in fact, according to the Lewis definition the proton, although an important and powerful acid, is but one of many possible acids. It is apparent that for Lewis acidity there is but one requirement—at least one available unfilled orbital in a valence shell. Any species is potentially a Lewis acid which has at least one available unfilled orbital in the valence shell of one of its atoms. Lewis acids are of several types.

1. Simple Cations. Theoretically all simple cations are potential Lewis acids, although their strength as acids varies within wide limits. Potassium ion (K^+) is a very weak Lewis acid, aluminum ion (Al^{+++}) a powerful Lewis acid. In general, we can expect the acid strength or coordinating ability of cations to increase with (a) an increase in positive charge on the ion, (b) an increase in nuclear charge for atoms in any horizontal period, (c) a decrease in ionic radius, and (d) a decrease in the number of shielding electron shells.

This means that Lewis acidity of simple cations tends to increase for the elements from left to right and from bottom to top in the periodic table. On the basis of the generalizations, we can predict the following representative sequences of increasing acid strength:

Order of Increasing Strength of Lewis Acids →

$$Fe^{++} < Fe^{+++}$$

$$K^+ < Na^+ < Li^+$$

$$Li^+ < Be^{++} < B^{+++}$$

From the beginning to end of each of the various series of transition elements, there is a build-up of nuclear charge with simultaneous contraction of ionic radius and no increase in the number of shielding shells. As a result many of the transition element cations are strong Lewis acids and tend to form a variety of complex ions.

Typical acid reactions of cations are shown in Table 4.1

TABLE 4.1. Typical Acid Reactions of Cations.

	Acid	Base		Coordinated Complex or Adduct
Ammonation	Ag^{+}	$+\ 2\ :NH_3$	→	$[H_3N:Ag:NH_3]^{+}$
Hydration	Al^{+++}	$+\ 6\ H_2O:$	→	$[Al(:OH_2)_6]^{+++}$
Alcoholation	Li^{+}	$+\ CH_3OH$	→	$[Li:O(CH_3)H]^{+}$
Ferricyanide Ion Formation	Fe^{+++}	$+\ 6\ :C{\equiv}N:^{-}$	→	$[Fe(:C{\equiv}N:)_6]^{\equiv}$

Actually, not all of the complexes, such as those in Table 4.1, formed by the arrangement of complexing groups around a simple central cation are held together by true covalent bonds. In many cases the bonds are of the ion-ion or ion-dipole type. The complexing groups are called *ligands*. Frequently more than one kind of ligand can be present in a single complex, and the different possible combinations into which cations and ligands can enter yield thousands of known complexes. Common ligands are such molecular bases as water, ammonia, and ethylene diamine and such ionic bases as hydroxide, cyanide, nitrate, carbonate, oxalate, sulfide, thiosulfate, thiocyanate, and halide ions. In accounting for the orderly grouping of ligands about a central ion, and also for the magnetic and spectral properties of complexes, chemists have achieved remarkable success in recent years through the application of the *ligand field* theory, an adaptation of the *crystal field* theory, originally developed by the physicists to account for the properties of crystals.

Of particular interest in organic chemistry are a group of reactive positive ions, thought to be active intermediates in many types of organic reactions. Among these are the nitronium ion $(:\underset{\cdot\cdot}{\overset{\cdot\cdot}{O}}-\overset{\oplus}{N}=\underset{\cdot\cdot}{\overset{\cdot\cdot}{O}})$, brominium ion $(:\underset{\cdot\cdot}{\overset{\cdot\cdot}{Br}}{}^{+})$, and the various carbonium (R^{+}) and acylium $\left(R-\overset{\overset{:O:}{\|}}{C}{}^{\oplus}\right)$ ions (see p. 107).

2. Compounds Whose Central Atom Has an Incomplete Octet. Among the most important Lewis acids are compounds whose central atom has less than a full octet of electrons. Typical examples are

$$\begin{array}{ccc} \begin{array}{c} \quad :\overset{\cdot\cdot}{F}: \\ :\underset{\cdot\cdot}{\overset{\cdot\cdot}{F}}:\underset{\cdot\cdot}{\overset{\cdot\cdot}{B}} \\ \quad :\underset{\cdot\cdot}{F}: \end{array} & \begin{array}{c} \quad :\overset{\cdot\cdot}{Cl}: \\ :\underset{\cdot\cdot}{\overset{\cdot\cdot}{Cl}}:\underset{\cdot\cdot}{\overset{\cdot\cdot}{B}} \\ \quad :\underset{\cdot\cdot}{Cl}: \end{array} & \begin{array}{c} \quad :\overset{\cdot\cdot}{Cl}: \\ :\underset{\cdot\cdot}{\overset{\cdot\cdot}{Cl}}:\underset{\cdot\cdot}{\overset{\cdot\cdot}{Al}} \\ \quad :\underset{\cdot\cdot}{Cl}: \end{array} \end{array}$$

Boron Trifluoride Boron Trichloride Aluminum Trichloride*

*Although anhydrous aluminum chloride exists at room temperature as the dimer (Al_2Cl_6) it behaves chemically as the monomer ($AlCl_3$).

```
                            ..            ..            CH3
 ..        ..              :O:           :Br:           ..
:Cl : Zn : Cl:          .. ..         .. ..         H3C : B
 ..        ..          :O : S        :Br : Fe            ..
                        .. ..         .. ..             CH3
                           :O:           :Br:
                            ..            ..
```

Zinc Chloride — Sulfur Trioxide — Ferric Bromide — Trimethyl Boron

Strength of these Lewis acids, in a general way* increases with

a. increase in nuclear charge of the central atom (for central atoms in the same horizontal period),
b. increase in the number and relative electronegativity of electronegative atoms attached to the central atom,
c. decrease in atomic radius of the central atom,
d. decrease in number of shielding electron shells in the central atom.

These rules are by no means completely general; some anomalies, such as the increased acidity toward most bases of trimethyl boron over boron trifluoride, are difficult to explain.

Coordination reactions of such acids are as follows:

a. Reaction of sulfur trioxide with basic oxides to form sulfate.

```
  Acid        Base      Coordinated Complex

   ..                       ..
  :O:                      :O:          =
 .. ..          ..      .. ..  ..
:O : S   +   :O:=  →   :O : S :O:
 .. ..          ..      .. ..  ..
  :O:                      :O:
   ..                       ..
```

b. The formation of boron trifluoride etherate (with ethyl ether).

*Actually, the order of acidity (or basicity) in any series of Lewis acids (or bases) often varies toward different bases (or acids). Frequently, the ease, purely from a spatial standpoint, with which the central atom can accommodate an additional group becomes the critical factor. In such cases acidity, especially toward large bases, tends to *increase* with *increasing* size of the central atom.

```
       Acid          Base          Coordinated Complex

        ..                           ..
       :F:         C2H5             :F:    C2H5
     .. ..        /               .. ..  ../
    :F:B   +  :O             →   :F—B:O
     .. ..     ..\                ..  ..   \
       :F:        C2H5              :F:    C2H5
        ..                           ..
```

c. The formation of complex fluoride ions, widely used in electrolytic melts.

```
       Acid            Base         Coordinated Complex

                                      ┌    ..      ┐=
                                      │   :F:      │
     ..     ..         ..             │ .. ..   .. │
    :F:Be:F:  +  2 :F:⁻      →        │:F:Be:F:    │
     ..     ..         ..             │ .. ..   .. │
                                      │   :F:      │
                                      └    ..      ┘
```

d. The coordination of aluminum fluoride with hydrogen fluoride to form fluoaluminic acid.

```
       Acid          Base         Coordinated Complex

        ..                            ..
       :F:                           :F:
     .. ..          ..             .. ..  ..
    :F:Al   +    :F—H    →        :F:Al:F—H
     .. ..          ..             .. ..  ..
       :F:                           :F:
        ..                            ..
```

The fact that hydrogen fluoride acts as a base toward aluminum trifluoride suggests that the latter is an extremely strong acid.

Often Lewis coordinations of this type are accompanied by a proton shift, as in the reaction of sulfur trioxide with water to form sulfuric acid:

```
       Acid          Base          Coordinated Complex

                                          H
        ..                                ..
       :O:           H                   :O:
     .. ..          /                 .. .. ..
    :O:S    +    :O          →       :O:S:O:H
     .. ..        ..\                 .. .. ..
       :O:           H                   :O:
        ..                                ..
```

Although the over-all reaction here is more complex, the key step is simply a Lewis acid-base reaction.

3. Compounds in Which the Octet of the Central Atom Can Be Expanded. Although carbon and silicon belong to the same family of elements, silicon tetrafluoride and silicon tetrachloride are tremendously more reactive than their carbon analogs, carbon tetrafluoride and carbon tetrachloride. The explanation is straightforward—the silicon, with its vacant *d* orbitals, can act as a Lewis acid by expanding its octet. This is illustrated by the reaction of silicon tetrafluoride with fluoride ion to form fluosilicate ion:

$$\underset{\text{Acid}}{SiF_4} + \underset{\text{Base}}{2\,F^-} \longrightarrow \underset{\text{Coordinated Complex}}{[SiF_6]^{=}}$$

With no available *d* orbitals, carbon cannot do this, in keeping with the fact that the elements in the first period of eight can accommodate no more than eight electrons in their valence shell.

Actually the silicon halides typify a large group of halides which, with vacant *d* orbitals, can expand their octets. Some examples are:

$SnCl_4$	$TiCl_4$	PCl_3	SF_4	SeF_4
Tin (IV) Chloride	Titanium (IV) Chloride	Phosphorus Trichloride	Sulfur Tetra-fluoride	Selenium Tetra-fluoride

These halides tend to form adducts with halide ions and with organic bases such as ethers $(R—\ddot{\underset{..}{O}}—R)$.

Halides of this type are vigorously hydrolyzed to form an oxy-acid (or oxide) of the central atom and the appropriate hydrogen halide. This reaction depends upon the ability of the halides to act as Lewis acids. The first step in the removal of each halogen atom is undoubtedly the acid-base coordination of the acid halide with the base water. This is followed by elimination of the hydrogen halide from the adduct. For the removal of the first chlorine in the hydrolysis of phosphorus trichloride, we believe the pathway or *mechanism* is

Acid — Base — Coordinated Complex or Adduct

$$:\ddot{Cl}:\ddot{P}(:\ddot{Cl}:)_2 + :\ddot{O}H_2 \longrightarrow \left[Cl_3P:\ddot{O}H_2 \right] \longrightarrow :\ddot{Cl}:\ddot{P}(:\ddot{Cl}:):\ddot{O}:H + H:\ddot{Cl}:$$

The two remaining chlorines are replaced similarly, with the ultimate formation of a total of three molecules of hydrogen chloride, and, after a proton shift, phosphorous acid $\left(H:\ddot{P}(:\ddot{O}:H)(:\ddot{O}:):\ddot{O}:H\right)$. Nitrogen trichloride ($NCl_3$), with a central atom (nitrogen) whose octet cannot be expanded, is hydrolyzed quite differently to ammonia and hypochlorous acid:

$$NCl_3 + 3HOH \rightarrow NH_3 + 3HOCl$$

One of the most important chemical reactions in high temperature metallurgical processes is that of silica (the gangue) with basic oxides (the flux) to form silicates (the slag). This is an acid-base reaction of the acid silica (SiO_2 polymer) with the base oxide ion:

Acid — Base — Coordinated Complex

$$(SiO_2)_X + X\ :\ddot{O}:^{=} \rightarrow \left[\ddot{O}::\ddot{Si}(:\ddot{O}:):\ddot{O}:^{=} \right]_X$$

The first step in the mechanism of this reaction is undoubtedly the coordination of oxide ion with silicon in the SiO_2 polymer; this requires an expansion of the silicon octet. Similar Lewis acid-base reactions are of fundamental importance in the manufacture of glass.

4. Compounds Having Multiply-bonded Acid Centers. There are many compounds, particularly organic, in which a multiply-bonded atom can accept a share in an electron pair with a synchronous shift in a pair of electrons of the multiple bond. By a slight extension of the Lewis concept, we can classify such compounds as Lewis acids. Although the atom involved does not, in a strict sense, have an unfilled orbital nevertheless an orbital is made available as the incoming base forces the intramolecular electron-pair shift.

A familiar example is carbon dioxide. Consider its neutralization by hydroxide ion to hydrogen carbonate ion:

$$\begin{array}{ccccc} \text{Acid} & & \text{Base} & & \text{Coordinated Complex} \\ \underset{\cdot\cdot}{\ddot{O}}::C::\underset{\cdot\cdot}{\ddot{O}} & + & {}^{-}:\underset{\cdot\cdot}{\ddot{O}}:H & \rightarrow & \begin{array}{c} \underset{\cdot\cdot}{\ddot{O}}::\underset{\cdot\cdot}{C}:\underset{\cdot\cdot}{\ddot{O}}:^{\ominus} \\ :\underset{\cdot\cdot}{O}: \\ H \end{array} \end{array}$$

Carbon dioxide accepts a pair of electrons from the base hydroxide ion in the process of coordination. The base attacks the *less electronegative* (and therefore more positive) of the double-bonded atoms and pushes a pair of electrons to the *more* electronegative atoms.* In fact, if resonance structures

of the type $\begin{array}{c} :\ddot{O}: \\ \underset{\cdot\cdot}{\ddot{O}}::\underset{\cdot\cdot}{\ddot{S}} \\ :\underset{\cdot\cdot}{O}: \end{array}$ are accepted for sulfur trioxide, the acid

*The hydrogen carbonate ion is a resonance hybrid. Writing of the second equivalent resonance structure will reveal that the increased electron density and negative charge supplied by the hydroxide ion are shared equally by the two oxygen atoms originally present in CO_2.

reactions of sulfur trioxide (p. 65) may be regarded as being of this same type.

All the typical addition reactions of aldehydes $\left(R-\overset{\overset{O}{\|}}{C}-H\right)$ and ketones $\left(R-\overset{\overset{O}{\|}}{C}-R'\right)$ fall into this class. In the addition of hydrogen cyanide to acetone to form acetone cyanohydrin, for example, the first step is the coordination of the base cyanide ion with the acid acetone:

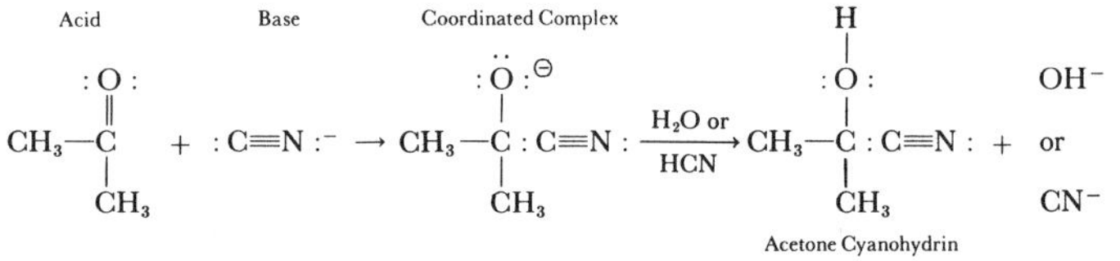

$$\underset{\text{Acid}}{CH_3-\overset{\overset{:\ddot{O}:}{\|}}{C}-CH_3} + \underset{\text{Base}}{:C{\equiv}N:^-} \rightarrow \underset{\text{Coordinated Complex}}{CH_3-\overset{:\ddot{O}:^{\ominus}}{\underset{CH_3}{C}}:C{\equiv}N:} \xrightarrow[HCN]{H_2O\ \text{or}} \underset{\text{Acetone Cyanohydrin}}{CH_3-\overset{H-:O:}{\underset{CH_3}{C}}:C{\equiv}N:} + \begin{matrix} OH^- \\ \text{or} \\ CN^- \end{matrix}$$

5. ***Elements with an Electron Sextet.*** To the extent that oxygen and sulfur *atoms* participate directly in chemical reactions, they may be regarded as Lewis acids. On this basis, the oxidation with sulfur of sulfite to thiosulfate and of sulfide to polysulfide ion can be classified as acid-base reactions:

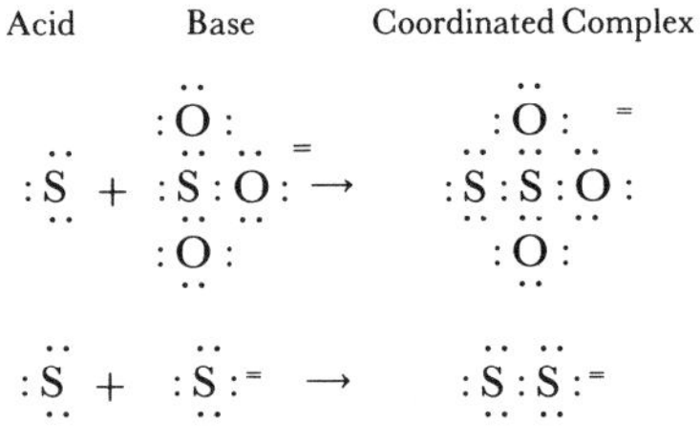

Acid		Base		Coordinated Complex
$:\ddot{\underset{..}{S}}$	+	$:\ddot{S}:\ddot{O}:^{=}$ (with $:\ddot{O}:$ above and $:\ddot{O}:$ below S)	→	$:\ddot{S}:\ddot{S}:\ddot{O}:^{=}$ (with $:\ddot{O}:$ above and $:\ddot{O}:$ below central S)
$:\ddot{\underset{..}{S}}$	+	$:\ddot{\underset{..}{S}}:^{=}$	→	$:\ddot{\underset{..}{S}}:\ddot{\underset{..}{S}}:^{=}$

Further Experimental Behavior of Acids and Bases

Besides neutralizing or coordinating bases, Lewis acids give additional experimental evidence that the relationship between Brønsted and Lewis acidity is not merely a formal one. Lewis acid-base titrations can be carried out in a variety of solvents. For example, boron trichloride and tin (IV) chloride, as acids, can be titrated against the bases pyridine and trimethylamine in chlorobenzene solution with crystal violet as indicator, just as hydrochloric acid can be titrated against sodium hydroxide in water solution. In both cases, the crystal violet is violet in basic and yellow in acid solution. A wide variety of other acids and bases, as well as other indicators such as butter yellow and thymol blue, can be used. Many Lewis acids, including carbon dioxide, sulfur dioxide, sulfur trioxide, tin (IV) chloride, aluminum chloride, and phosphorus trichloride, when added to water give solutions which test acid.

The Lewis concept has revolutionized not only the theory, but also the practice, of acid catalysis, particularly in organic chemistry. Aluminum chloride, boron trifluoride, sulfur trioxide, and ferric bromide are all important acid catalysts, used interchangeably for many reactions with Brønsted acids such as sulfuric acid and hydrogen fluoride. Often the Lewis acid catalysts are far superior, and in some cases are effective for reactions where Brønsted acids are useless.

chapter five

BASE DISPLACEMENT REACTIONS

(or, Organic Chemistry is Back in the Ball Park)

How does the Brønsted concept interpret the Lewis acid-base or coordination reactions discussed in the last chapter? It stands before them as the ox before the sewing machine. Because they do not involve proton, it simply does not pretend to deal with them.

Nevertheless, the Brønsted concept is extremely useful. In elegant fashion, it explains, correlates, and systematizes a vast and significant body of chemical reactions. How does the Lewis concept interpret protolysis reactions? This is a crucial question. And the answer is easy—in a refreshingly logical, simple, and straightforward manner.

Brønsted Protolysis Reactions as Base Displacements

In the Lewis system, hydrogen chloride is not a true acid, since the hydrogen has no available orbital in which to accommodate an additional pair of electrons. But we can conveniently consider hydrogen chloride as a coordinated complex made up of the acid portion proton (H^+) and the base portion chloride ion ($:\ddot{\underset{..}{Cl}}:^-$). In fact, any potential Brønsted acid HA may be viewed as a coordinated complex, made up of the acid portion H^+ and the base portion $:A^-$.

Let's look at Table 5.1 which treats a few representative examples of various types of Brønsted protolysis reactions from this standpoint.

Every Brønsted Protolysis Is a Simple Base Displacement

Each of the five reactions shown is a base displacement. And each proceeds *essentially to completion to the right* because the *displacing base* on the left is *much stronger* than the base it displaces.

In the ionization of an acid, the displacing base is the solvent. In typical neutralization reactions of a strong acid with a strong base, the conjugate base of the solvent displaces the solvent. In basic hydrolysis, the displacing base displaces hydroxide ion.

In the hydrolysis of sodium acetate, for example, the displacing base is acetate ion:

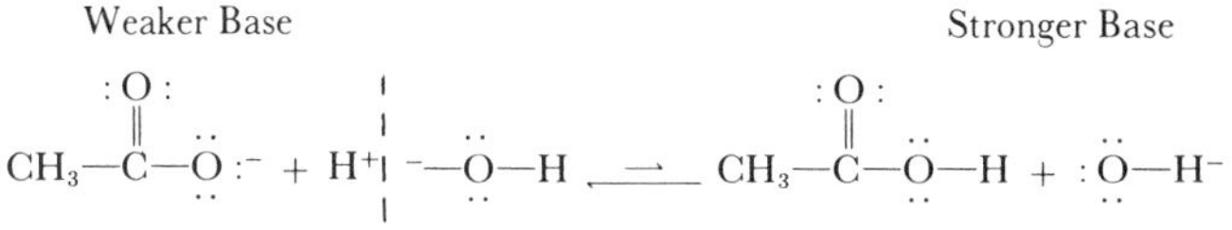

Weaker Base | Stronger Base

$$CH_3-\overset{\overset{:O:}{\|}}{C}-\ddot{\underset{..}{O}}:^- + H^+|^- -\ddot{\underset{..}{O}}-H \rightleftharpoons CH_3-\overset{\overset{:O:}{\|}}{C}-\ddot{\underset{..}{O}}-H + :\ddot{\underset{..}{O}}-H^-$$

But acetate ion is a weaker base than hydroxide ion, so the hydrolysis proceeds to the right to the extent of only a few per cent. Conversely, in the neutralization of acetic acid with sodium hydroxide, the considerably stronger base hydroxide ion displaces the weaker base acetate ion, and the reaction proceeds far to the right:

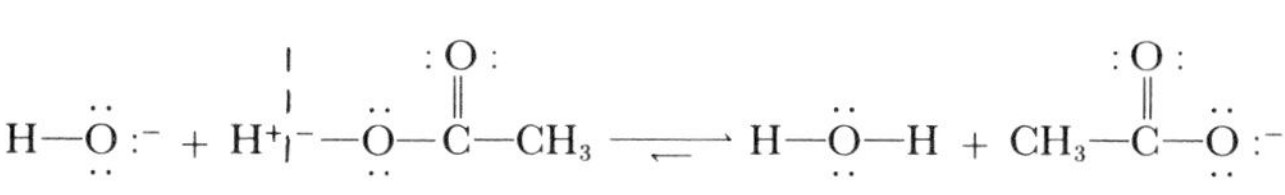

$$H-\ddot{\underset{..}{O}}:^- + H^+|^- -\ddot{\underset{..}{O}}-\overset{\overset{:O:}{\|}}{C}-CH_3 \rightleftharpoons H-\ddot{\underset{..}{O}}-H + CH_3-\overset{\overset{:O:}{\|}}{C}-\ddot{\underset{..}{O}}:^-$$

TABLE 5.1. Some Brønsted Protolysis Reactions Viewed as Base Displacements

Reaction	Much stronger base	+	Coordinated Complex: Acid Portion	Coordinated Complex: Base Portion	displaces	weaker base
Ionization	$H_2\ddot{O}:$	+	H^+	$—:\ddot{Cl}:^-$	→	$H_2\ddot{O}H^+$ + $:\ddot{Cl}:^-$
Neutralization	$H—\ddot{O}:^-$	+	H^+	$—\ddot{O}H_2$	→	$H_2\ddot{O}$ + $H_2\ddot{O}$
Neutralization	$CH_3—C(=O)—\ddot{O}:^-$	+	H^+	$—\ddot{O}(H)—C(=O)—CH_3$	→	$CH_3—C(=O)—\ddot{O}—H$ + $CH_3—C(=O)—\ddot{O}—H$
Neutralization	$H—\ddot{N}(H):^-$	+	H^+	$—N(H)(H)—H$	→	$H—\ddot{N}(H)—H$ + $H—\ddot{N}(H)—H$
Hydrolysis	$H—\ddot{N}(H):^-$	+	H^+	$—\ddot{O}—H^-$	→	$H—\ddot{N}(H)—H$ + $:\ddot{O}—H^-$

The weaker base water does not effect substantial displacement of the stronger base ammonia in the hydrolysis of ammonium ion (in salts such as ammonium chloride):

Weaker Base   Stronger Base

$$\underset{H}{\overset{H}{\diagdown}}\ddot{O}: + \overset{+}{H}\,\Big|\,\text{—}\underset{H}{\overset{H}{|}}{N}\text{—}H \rightleftharpoons \underset{H}{\overset{H}{\diagdown}}\ddot{O}.\,H^{+} + :\underset{H}{\overset{H}{|}}{N}\text{—}H$$

This means, again, that the hydrolysis is only slight.

In fact, we can make this broad generalization: Whenever a base B : or B :$^-$ is added to a coordinated complex H—A or H—A$^+$, base displacement can occur. If B : or B :$^-$ is much stronger than A :$^-$ or A :, this displacement will be essentially complete. If B : or B :$^-$ is much weaker than A :$^-$ or A :, displacement will be very slight. If base B : or B :$^-$ has exactly the same strength as A :$^-$ or A :, the reaction will go exactly half way to completion (K = unity). We can interpret and predict all Brønsted protolyses from this direct and logical standpoint.

This gives new meaning to the acid-base chart on page 19. It tells us that any base can displace over 50 per cent of any base above it in the base list. Any base can displace any base below it only less than 50 per cent. And in a general way, the extent of reaction can be predicted by the distance between the two bases in the list.

In organic reactions, the function of base catalysts is usually to displace the reactive base which participates in the main reaction, at least to a sufficient extent to permit the main reaction to occur. For example, in the base-catalyzed aldol condensation, as well as in the haloform reaction and other base-catalyzed halogenations of aldehydes and ketones, the function of the base catalyst is to displace the reactive carbanion which functions as the base in the main reaction. In the aldol condensation of acetaldehyde with hydroxide ion as catalyst, the hydroxide ion displaces acetaldehyde carbanion in low (but sufficient for reaction with another molecule of acetaldehyde) concentration.

Weaker Base: $H{-}\ddot{O}{:}^{-} + H^{+}|^{-}{-}CH_2{-}C({=}O){-}H \rightleftharpoons H{-}\ddot{O}{-}H +$ Stronger Base: $\{ {:}\overset{\ominus}{C}H_2{-}C({=}O){-}H \leftrightarrow CH_2{=}C({-}\ddot{O}{:}^{\ominus}){-}H \}$

Similarly in the Claisen condensation the base catalyst (usually ethoxide ion) displaces the reactive carbanion which serves as the displacing base in the main reaction. In the Claisen condensation of ethyl acetate, for example, the displaced base is the carbanion of ethyl acetate, listed as the first nucleophile in Table 5.5, p. 100.

Base Displacements at Hydrogen

Take another look at the base displacements just discussed. Every one is a base displacement at hydrogen. In each case the displacing base attacks a hydrogen atom, displacing the base in the coordinated complex from proton. In fact, *all Brønsted protolysis reactions are base displacements at hydrogen.* Cannot base displacements occur at elements other than hydrogen? The answer, most assuredly, is YES!

Just as quick examples, consider from this standpoint the reaction of chlorine with sodium hydroxide to form hypochlorous acid, that of chlorine with solutions of iodides to liberate iodine, and the iodination of acetaldehyde carbanion:

Base		Coordinated Complex			Base
$H{-}\ddot{\underset{..}{O}}:^-$	+	$:\ddot{\underset{..}{Cl}}^+ \mid -\ddot{\underset{..}{Cl}}:^-$	$\longrightarrow$	$H{-}\ddot{\underset{..}{O}}{-}\ddot{\underset{..}{Cl}}:$	$+:\ddot{\underset{..}{Cl}}:^-$
$:\ddot{\underset{..}{I}}:^-$	+	$:\ddot{\underset{..}{Cl}}^+ \mid -\ddot{\underset{..}{Cl}}:^-$	$\longrightarrow$	$:\ddot{\underset{..}{I}}{-}\ddot{\underset{..}{Cl}}:$	$+:\ddot{\underset{..}{Cl}}:^-$
$:\ddot{\underset{..}{I}}:^-$	+	$:\ddot{\underset{..}{I}}^+ \mid -\ddot{\underset{..}{Cl}}:^-$	$\longrightarrow$	$:\ddot{\underset{..}{I}}{-}\ddot{\underset{..}{I}}:$	$+:\ddot{\underset{..}{Cl}}:^-$

$$H{-}\overset{\overset{:O:}{\|}}{C}{-}\underset{H}{\overset{H}{C}}:^{\ominus} \;+\; :\ddot{\underset{..}{I}}^+ \mid -\ddot{\underset{..}{I}}:^- \longrightarrow H{-}\overset{\overset{:\ddot{O}:}{\|}}{C}{-}\underset{H}{\overset{H}{C}}{-}\ddot{\underset{..}{I}}: + :\ddot{\underset{..}{I}}:^-$$

All Brønsted protolysis reactions may be viewed either as proton transfers or as base displacements at hydrogen. Often there are advantages in adopting one viewpoint or the other. Play it cagey, be flexible and versatile, taking whichever slant is most helpful in a given case. But undoubtedly, one advantage of the base-displacement viewpoint is this: it provides the intellectual link between Brønsted acid-base reactions and the host of important base-displacement reactions that make up a large part of organic chemistry. It brings organic chemistry back into the ball park along with inorganic chemistry.

Nucleophilic Displacements at Carbon

Base displacements at carbon constitute the largest of the major classes of organic reactions. In general, stronger bases (as measured by equilibria in competition for proton) displace weaker bases at carbon, just as they do at hydrogen. By far the most important carbon compounds in which these displacements occur are the alkyl halides, RX. As weak bases, halide ions are fairly completely displaced by a wide variety of stronger bases. In order to analyze these reactions critically, let's take a look at the electronic structure of a simple alkyl halide, methyl bromide:

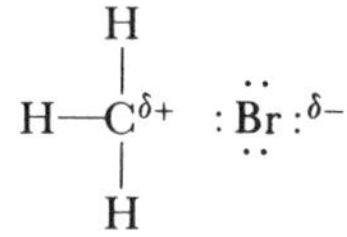

$$\begin{array}{c} \text{H} \\ | \\ \text{H—C}^{\delta+} \quad :\ddot{\underset{\cdot\cdot}{\text{Br}}}:^{\delta-} \\ | \\ \text{H} \end{array}$$

The methyl bromide molecule has much in common with that of hydrogen bromide. Bromine is much more electronegative than methyl group, and, on the average, the bonding electron pair is displaced away from the carbon toward the bromine atom. As a result, the molecule is polar, and the carbon is at the electron-deficient or positive end of the dipole, just as is hydrogen in hydrogen bromide. In fact, like hydrogen bromide, methyl bromide may be regarded as a coordinated complex, made up of the strong acid methyl carbonium ion, and the weak base bromide ion. And the well-known reaction of methyl bromide with hydroxide ion to form methyl alcohol is truly a base displacement at carbon, with the base hydroxide ion displacing the base bromide ion:

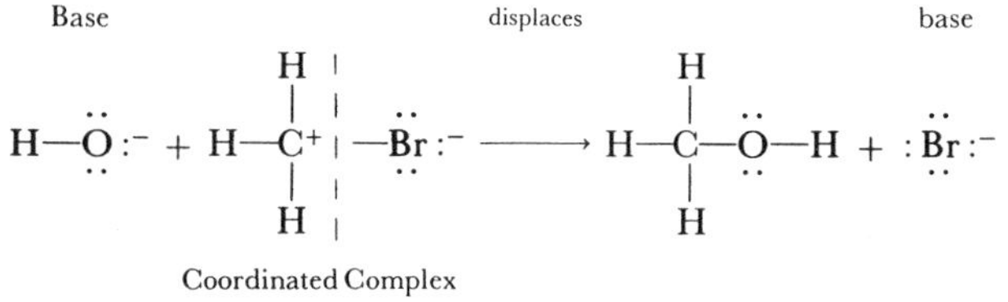

Base displaces base

$$\text{H—}\ddot{\underset{\cdot\cdot}{\text{O}}}:^{-} + \text{H—}\overset{\text{H}}{\underset{\text{H}}{\overset{|}{\underset{|}{\text{C}}}}}{}^{+} \,|\, \text{—}\ddot{\underset{\cdot\cdot}{\text{Br}}}:^{-} \longrightarrow \text{H—}\overset{\text{H}}{\underset{\text{H}}{\overset{|}{\underset{|}{\text{C}}}}}\text{—}\ddot{\underset{\cdot\cdot}{\text{O}}}\text{—H} + :\ddot{\underset{\cdot\cdot}{\text{Br}}}:^{-}$$

Coordinated Complex

Indeed, a mole of methyl bromide does, in time, "neutralize" a mole of sodium hydroxide, just as does hydrogen bromide, for the products in both cases are neutral to litmus.

But there are significant differences between the two reactions. First of all, the reaction of methyl bromide with hydroxide ion is much slower than are base displacements involving hydrogen bromide. Proton transfer reactions require only the shift of a nucleus (H^+) without any attendant electrons. The simple nature of such reactions is perhaps primarily responsible for the fact that proton transfers are facile and rapid, and lead to mobile equilibria. Rarely are chemists concerned about the rate of protolysis reactions, but rather about equilibria.

Base displacements at carbon, on the other hand, are much slower. Here we are usually concerned chiefly about the rate of reaction, especially because the displacements used in synthetic organic chemistry are necessarily those in which either (1) the displacing base is stronger than the displaced base or (2) the displacing base is only slightly weaker, and reaction conditions can be controlled to force the formation of the desired product. In fact, chemists tend to think of the reactivity of displacing bases in organic reactions in terms of the *rate* at which they react, rather than of the precise extent (at equilibrium) to which they react. This is at least one reason why chemists use other than the usual acid-base terminology in dealing with polar reactions at carbon.

The typical displacing species are all *electron-pair donors* or *basic reagents* which attack electron deficient sites—species, in other words, which can share one of their electron pairs with a nucleus. We call all such electron-pair donors or basic reagents *nucleophilic* (Greek, nucleus-loving) *reagents* or *nucleophiles*.

In a typical base displacement at carbon, the attacking base is called a *nucleophile*, the species attacked or coordinated complex is the *substrate*, the displaced base is the *leaving group*, and the reaction itself is called a *nucleophilic substitution*. Thus we can label the nucleophilic substitution of bromide by hydroxide ion in methyl bromide as follows:

$$\underset{\text{Nucleophile}}{H-\ddot{\underset{..}{O}}:^-} + \underset{\text{Substrate or Coordinated Complex}}{H-\underset{H}{\overset{H}{\underset{|}{\overset{|}{C}}}}-\ddot{\underset{..}{Br}}:} \longrightarrow \underset{\text{Product}}{H-\underset{H}{\overset{H}{\underset{|}{\overset{|}{C}}}}-\ddot{\underset{..}{O}}-H} + \underset{\text{Leaving Group}}{:\ddot{\underset{..}{Br}}:^-}$$

The reactivity of the nucleophile, or its nucleophilicity, is measured by the *rate* of its reaction with a substrate; basicity, as we have seen, is measured by the position of equilibrium in the competition of two nucleophiles for a given substrate (competitive protolysis, p. 17, in the case of Brønsted basicity). We might perhaps expect nucleophilicity to parallel basicity. And, as a rule, the strongest bases are the best nucleophiles. In fact, there is a fairly close correspondence between nucleophilicity and basicity, especially for any family of nucleophiles whose attacking atoms are the same atoms, or are in the same horizontal row in the periodic table. Thus, for example, we could predict (see p. 19) these orders of decreasing nucleophilicity, which are established experimentally:*

$$H_3C{:}^- > H_2\ddot{N}{:}^- > H\ddot{O}{:}^- > {:}\ddot{F}{:}^-$$

$$C_2H_5\ddot{O}{:}^- > H\ddot{O}{:}^- > C_6H_5\ddot{O}{:}^- > CH_3C(=O)\ddot{O}{:}^- > H\ddot{O}H > ClO_4^-$$

The major reversals in the order of relative nucleophilicities as compared with Brønsted basicities are found in families of nucleophiles in which the attacking atoms are members of the same family in the periodic table. Here the orders of relative nucleophilicity are exactly those predicted on the basis of relative electronegativity—the stronger nucleophilic push is supplied by the less electronegative atoms or groups, i.e., nucleophilicity increases from top to bottom in any family:

*Relative orders of nucleophilicity, like relative orders of basicity (see p. 65) are not invariable. For nucleophiles, relative orders of reactivity sometimes change with changes in the spatial (steric) effects involved in reaction toward different substrates.

$$:\ddot{F}:^- < :\ddot{Cl}:^- < :\ddot{Br}:^- < :\ddot{I}:^-$$

$$H—\ddot{O}:^- < H—\ddot{S}:^- < H—\ddot{Se}:^-$$

$$R—\ddot{O}—R < R—\ddot{S}—R < R—\ddot{Se}—R$$

Thus we have no hydrogen halide problem (see p. 50) in dealing with relative nucleophilicities.

For an interesting example of the difference between nucleophilicity and basicity, let's look at the competition between iodide ion and ethoxide ion in reaction with methyl bromide. Iodide ion reacts faster than ethoxide ion; i.e., it is a *more reactive nucleophile*. But in time ethoxide ion displaces iodide ion almost completely; it is *more basic*. As a result in the initial stages of the competition more methyl iodide is produced, but at equilibrium the final product is largely methyl ethyl ether ($CH_3—O—C_2H_5$) (see Fig. 5.1).

Bromide ion is a weak base—it is rather completely displaced in methyl bromide by hydroxide ion; i.e., conversion to methyl alcohol is substantially complete. It is also displaced rather rapidly. In fact, we find excellent general correlation here—the less basic the leaving group the more readily it is

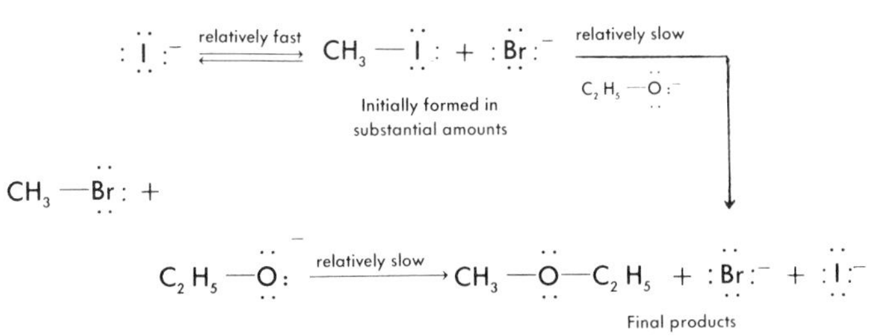

$$CH_3—\ddot{Br}: + \begin{cases} :\ddot{I}:^- \xrightleftharpoons{\text{relatively fast}} CH_3—\ddot{I}: + :\ddot{Br}:^- \text{ (Initially formed in substantial amounts)} \xrightarrow[C_2H_5—\ddot{O}:^-]{\text{relatively slow}} \\ C_2H_5—\ddot{O}:^- \xrightarrow{\text{relatively slow}} CH_3—\ddot{O}—C_2H_5 + :\ddot{Br}:^- + :\ddot{I}:^- \text{ (Final products)} \end{cases}$$

Fig. 5.1. Competition Between Iodide and Ethoxide Ions in Reaction with Methyl Bromide.

displaced by an attacking nucleophile. Thus we can write the following order of increasing rate of displacement of various leaving groups in nucleophilic substitutions (see list of bases in chart p. 19):

$$H{-}\ddot{N}{-}H^- < C_2H_5{-}\ddot{O}{:}^- < H{-}\ddot{O}{:}^- < CH_3{-}\overset{\overset{\large :O:}{\|}}{C}{-}\ddot{O}{:}^- <$$

$$:\ddot{F}{:}^- < :\ddot{Cl}{:}^- < :\ddot{Br}{:}^- < :\ddot{I}{:}^- < Ar{-}\overset{\overset{\large :\ddot{O}:}{|}}{\underset{\underset{\large :\ddot{O}:}{|}}{S}}{-}\ddot{O}{:}^-$$

Hence, the most reactive substrates are those with weak bases such as halide ion (X^-), sulfate ion ($SO_4^=$), aryl sulfate ions ($ArSO_4^-$), and alkyl or aryl sulfonate ions (RSO_3^- or $ArSO_3^-$) as leaving groups. It is not surprising, therefore, that many of the important nucleophilic substitutions at carbon occur in alkyl halides (RX), alkyl and aryl sulfates $\left(RO{-}\overset{\overset{O}{|}}{\underset{\underset{O}{|}}{S}}{-}OR \text{ and } ArO{-}\overset{\overset{O}{|}}{\underset{\underset{O}{|}}{S}}{-}OR\right)$, and alkyl or aryl sulfonates $\left(R{-}\overset{\overset{O}{|}}{\underset{\underset{O}{|}}{S}}{-}OR \text{ or } Ar{-}\overset{\overset{O}{|}}{\underset{\underset{O}{|}}{S}}{-}OR\right)$. In certain important nucleophilic substitutions, the leaving groups tertiary amines or water are displaced from such ions as tetramethylammonium $\left(CH_3{-}\overset{\overset{CH_3}{|}}{\underset{\underset{CH_3}{|}}{N}}{-}CH_3^+\right)$ or alkyl oxonium $\left(R{-}\overset{\overset{H}{|}}{O}{-}H^+\right)$ ions.

With these principles in mind, we could predict most of the representative nucleophilic substitutions listed in Table 5.2.

TABLE 5.2 Some Representative Nucleophilic Substitution Reactions

Reaction	Nucleophile		Substrate		Product		Leaving Group
General	$N:^-$	+	R—L	→	R—N	+	$L:^-$
Alcohol Synthesis	$H—O:^-$	+	R—X:	→	R—O—H	+	$:X:^-$
Williamson Ether Synthesis	$R—O:^-$	+	R—X:	→	R—O—R	+	$:X:^-$
Nitrile Synthesis	$:C≡N:^-$	+	R—X:	→	R—C≡N:	+	$:X:^-$
Ester Synthesis	$R—C(=O)—O:^-$	+	R′—X:	→	R—C(=O)—OR′	+	$:X:^-$
Thiol Synthesis	$H—S:^-$	+	R—X:	→	H—S—R	+	$:X:^-$
Thioether Synthesis	$R—S:^-$	+	R′—X:	→	R—S—R′	+	$:X:^-$
Azide Synthesis	$:N≡N—N:^-$	+	R—X:	→	R—N—N≡N:	+	$:X:^-$
Hydride Reduction	$H:^-$	+	R—X:	→	R—H	+	$:X:^-$
Wurtz Reaction	$R:^-$	+	R—X:	→	R—R	+	$:X:^-$
Alkyne Synthesis	$R—C≡C:^-$	+	R′—X:	→	R—C≡C—R′	+	$:X:^-$
Hofmann Synthesis	$H—N(H)(H):$	+	R—X:	→	$H—N(H)(H)—R^+$	+	$:X:^-$
Amine Displacement	$H—O:^-$	+	$CH_3—N(CH_3)(CH_3)—CH_3^+$	→	$CH_3—O—H$	+	$(CH_3)_3N:$
Alkyl Halide Synthesis	$:X:^-$	+	$R—O(H)—H^+$	→	R—X:	+	H—O—H

Many Nucleophilic Substitutions Proceed with Inversion

We might expect that, from an electrostatic standpoint, negatively charged hydroxide ion would be likely to attack the carbon atom in methyl bromide on the side to the rear of the negatively charged bromine atom, rather than head-on. Likewise, it can be shown that attack of the hydroxide ion on the tetrahedral face of the carbon atom opposite the bromine permits a smooth and feasible geometrical transition from methyl bromide to alcohol, i.e. from reactant to product.

It is no surprise, therefore, that studies on a wide variety of substrates in which the carbon attacked is linked to four different groups have proved the following: many typical nucleophilic substitutions proceed with inversion of configuration at the carbon atom. The only plausible explanation of this fact is based on the requirement that the nucleophile hit the carbon under attack from the back side (at the tetrahedral face opposite the leaving group).

S_N2 Reactions

In order to understand why this is true, and also what is meant by inversion, let's look at a three-dimensional picture for the accepted mechanism for the transition from reactants to products in a typical nucleophilic displacement (Fig. 5.2).

The nucleophile Z :⁻ attacks the carbon from the back side.

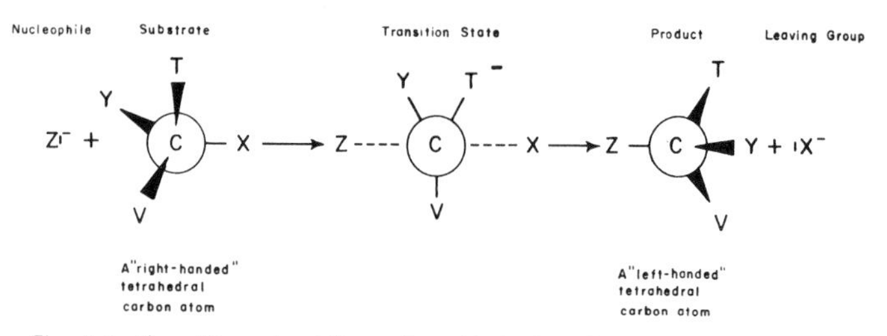

Fig. 5.2. Three-Dimensional Picture for a Typical Nucleophilic Displacement with Inversion. (Bar on Z^- and on X^- represents an unshared electron pair.)

As Z:$^-$ approaches, it begins to form a covalent bond with the carbon and the C—X bond begins to break. At the same time, T, Y, and V recede, at one stage passing through a planar "spoke" arrangement.

The complex in the middle represents a sort of halfway point in the reaction, beyond which the system is more likely to progress toward the products than to retreat to the reactants. It is called the activated complex or *transition state.* It shows both Z and X partially bonded to C along a line through the center of the carbon nucleus and perpendicular to the single, central plane in which the carbon atom and all three groups T, Y, and V are located. The three bonds from carbon to T, Y, and V radiate out from the carbon like the spokes of a wheel, at angles of 120° to each other.

Now, as the reaction rolls downhill to form the final products, X:$^-$ breaks away from the carbon, and the groups T, Y, and V flip over to the other side of the central plane. This process, known as an *inversion*, has actually turned the molecule inside out like an umbrella in a hurricane. The incoming Z has definitely not taken the configurational position in the tetrahedron originally occupied by X. A reaction that yields a product whose configuration is opposite to that of the reactant is said to proceed with *inversion.*

Typical nucleophilic substitutions of the type described, which proceed with inversion, are called S_N2 (*bimolecular nucleophilic substitution*) reactions. The mechanism is considered a bimolecular one because both the nucleophile and the substrate are synchronously involved in bond-making or breaking in the rate-determining step.

Steric Factors

Now consider the probability of back side attack by a nucleophile such as H—$\ddot{\underset{\cdot\cdot}{O}}$:$^-$ on the central carbon in tertiary (or *t*-) butyl bromide:

```
                               H
                               |
                            H—C—H
                       H       |
        ..             |       |
    H—O:⁻  +  H———C———C———Br
        ..             |       |
                       H       |
                            H—C—H
                               |
                               H
```

The required transition state, with five relatively bulky groups crowded around the central carbon, would be a high energy or unstable structure and could be formed only extremely slowly. The result is that for *t*-butyl bromide the rates of bimolecular nucleophilic substitution reactions are greatly retarded (actually to less than a thousandth of their value for methyl bromide) because of this spatial or steric factor*, and other reaction mechanisms which proceed at a more rapid rate may begin to take over.

S_N1 Reactions

One of these is suggested by the fact that solvents such as water and acetic acid strongly solvate halide ions and that silver ion (Ag^+) is a powerful Lewis acid in coordinating halide ion. If the reaction is run in water or in acetic acid, or if silver hydroxide rather than sodium hydroxide is used, the *t*-butyl bromide may be at least partially ionized by solvation or coordination of the bromide ion to form a small equi-

*The importance of steric factors understandably increases in the order

```
      H               R               R
      |               |               |
    R—C—X     <     R—C—X     <     R—C—X
      |               |               |
      H               H               R
Primary Halides  Secondary Halides  Tertiary Halides
```

librium concentration of the *t*-butyl carbonium ion

$$(CH_3-\overset{\overset{\large CH_3}{|}}{\underset{\underset{\large CH_3}{|}}{C^+}})$$

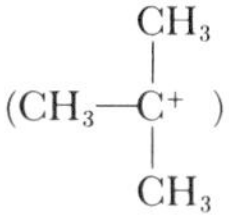

. This possibility is enhanced by the fact shown by many studies that the stability, and therefore the ease of formation, of carbonium ion increases in the same order as the importance of steric factors:

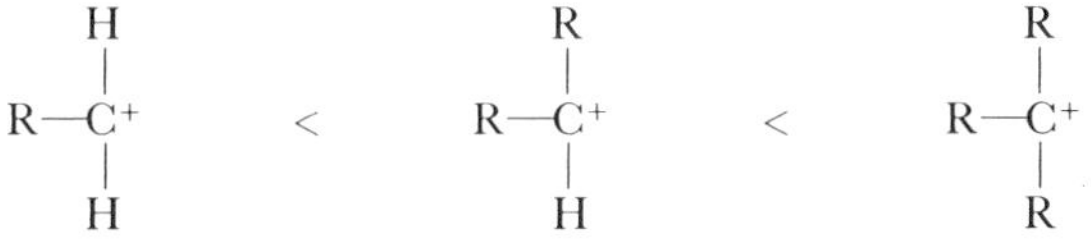

$$R-\overset{\overset{\large H}{|}}{\underset{\underset{\large H}{|}}{C^+}} \quad < \quad R-\overset{\overset{\large R}{|}}{\underset{\underset{\large H}{|}}{C^+}} \quad < \quad R-\overset{\overset{\large R}{|}}{\underset{\underset{\large R}{|}}{C^+}}$$

Primary Carbonium Ion — Secondary Carbonium Ion — Tertiary Carbonium Ion

The effect of the electron-releasing R groups is to stabilize the carbonium ion through charge dispersal (p. 55).

We can represent the proposed ionization reactions as follows (HA = water or acetic acid):

$$\text{Solvation}\ CH_3-\overset{\overset{\large CH_3}{|}}{\underset{\underset{\large CH_3}{|}}{C}}-Br\text{- - -}HA \rightleftharpoons CH_3-\overset{\overset{\large CH_3}{|}}{\underset{\underset{\large CH_3}{|}}{C^+}} + [:\ddot{\underset{\cdot\cdot}{Br}}:-HA]^-$$

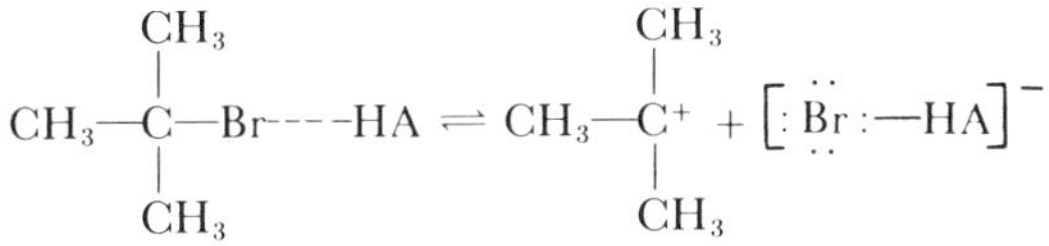

$$\text{Lewis Coordination}\ CH_3-\overset{\overset{\large CH_3}{|}}{\underset{\underset{\large CH_3}{|}}{C}}-Br\text{- - -}Ag^+ \rightleftharpoons CH_3-\overset{\overset{\large CH_3}{|}}{\underset{\underset{\large CH_3}{|}}{C^+}} + AgBr$$

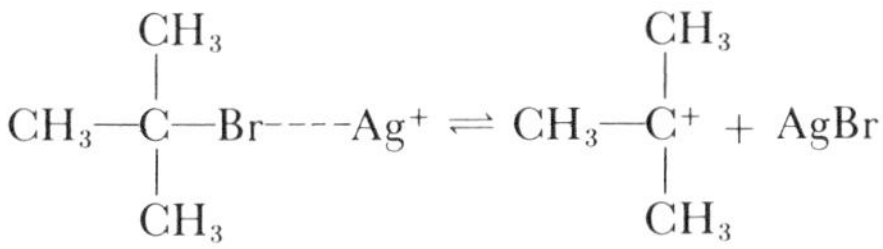

We believe, on good evidence, that the *t*-butyl carbonium ion, more or less in free form (probably extensively solvated), is a highly reactive transient intermediate which undergoes reaction as rapidly as it is formed. As a powerful Lewis acid, it can coordinate instantly with hydroxide ion to form the substituted product, *t*-butyl alcohol:

$$\mathrm{CH_3-\overset{\displaystyle CH_3}{\underset{\displaystyle CH_3}{\overset{|}{\underset{|}{C^+}}}}} + :\ddot{\underset{\cdot\cdot}{O}}-\mathrm{H}^- \rightarrow \mathrm{CH_3-\overset{\displaystyle CH_3}{\underset{\displaystyle CH_3}{\overset{|}{\underset{|}{C}}}}-OH}$$

The carbonium ion is pictured as a planar structure, and we might expect that hydroxide ion could attack from either side. Studies on the reactions of pure right- or left-handed *t*-alkyl halides containing three different alkyl groups confirm this view; the alcohol formed in this reaction is a mixture of the two possible configurational types, as shown in Fig. 5.3.

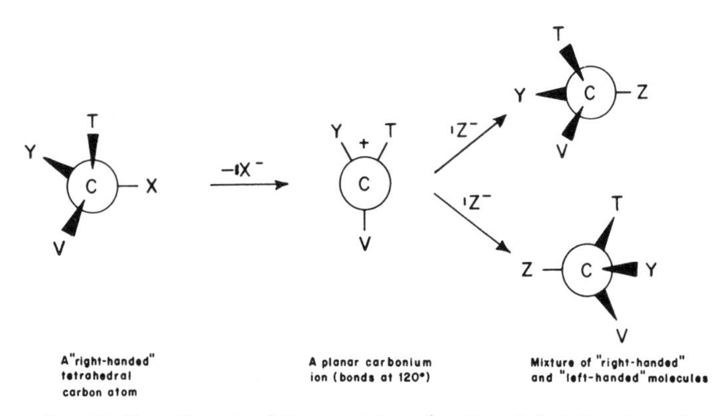

Fig. 5.3. Three-Dimensional Representation of a Typical S_N1 Reaction. (Bar on X^- and on Z^- represents an unshared electron pair.)

Nucleophilic substitutions which proceed through initial formation of carbonium ions are called S_N1 (*unimolecular nucleophilic substitutions*); *unimolecular* because the substrate, but not the nucleophile, is involved in the rate-determining step (in this case the first step) of the reaction. The nucleophilic substitution is effected in two steps—and somewhat indirectly.

E1 Reactions

A carbonium ion can, however, undergo a second type of reaction with a base such as hydroxide ion. Most carbonium ions can be Brønsted or protonic as well as Lewis acids. Electron shift toward the positive carbon greatly increases the acidity of the hydrogens—to the point in fact where a proton is readily donated;

```
                          H                               H
                          |                               |
              H       H—C—H                  H     H—C—H
              |           |                   |           |
H—O:⁻  +H ¦——C——————C⁺ ——→ H—O—H + C=====C
              |           |                   |           |
              H       H—C—H                  H     H—C—H
                          |                               |
                          H                               H
```

With *t*-butyl carbonium ion, the product is the olefin isobutylene. In fact, like all protolyses this step is actually a base displacement with the stronger base hydroxide ion replacing the weaker base isobutylene from its combination with the acid proton.

The over-all result of the reaction is the elimination of HBr from the CH_3—$C(CH_3)_2$—Br molecule.

```
                 CH₃
                 |
from the CH₃—C—Br molecule.
                 |
                 CH₃
```

```
             H                                H
             |                                |
     H    H—C—H                     H    H—C
     |       |                        |      ||
H—C————C—Br ——→ H—C—————C        + HBr
     |       |                        |       |
     H    H—C—H                     H    H—C—H
             |                                |
             H                                H
```

The reaction is called an *elimination*, and because only *t*-butyl bromide, and not hydroxide ion, is involved in the slow or rate-determining step, it is a *unimolecular* elimination, E1.

To the extent that the conversion of a halide to an alcohol proceeds through the carbonium ion or unimolecular mechanism, always more or less olefin will be formed simultaneously. Although the ratio of alcohol to olefin is determined largely by the exact structure of the carbonium ion involved, we can control it to an extent by choice of operating temperature, of solvent, and of concentration of reactants.

The E2 Reaction

Now suppose that hydroxide ion is added to *t*-butyl bromide in a poorly solvating solvent (such as ethyl alcohol) in the absence of a coordinating cation of the type Ag^+. In this case, the product of reaction is almost exclusively isobutylene.

The proposed mechanism for its formation is based on the fact that the methyl hydrogens, because of electron drift in the molecule toward the highly electronegative bromine atom, are somewhat acidic. Loss of proton to hydroxide ion could set into synchronous motion a chain of events leading to the formation of isobutylene and elimination of bromide ion:

$$H{-}\ddot{\underset{..}{O}}{:}^- + H{-}CH_2{-}C(CH_3)_2{-}\ddot{\underset{..}{Br}}{:} \longrightarrow H{-}\ddot{\underset{..}{O}}{-}H + (H)_2C{=}C(CH_3)_2 + {:}\ddot{\underset{..}{Br}}{:}^-$$

The over-all result is an elimination of HBr from the *t*-butyl bromide molecule, so the reaction is called an *elimination*. Since hydroxide ion, along with the *t*-butyl bromide molecule, is involved in the single step in the proposed reaction mechanism, we can call the reaction a *bimolecular elimination*, E2. It is interesting to note that the actual displacing base on this "sterically hindered" substrate is the smallest possible base, a pair of electrons, and is already present in the halide molecule.

Actually, other nucleophiles besides hydroxide ion can (as Brønsted bases) accept a proton from alkyl halides to set in motion the proposed synchronous E2 mechanism. And they can certainly displace olefins from combination with proton in carbonium ions. As a result, in a very general sense nucleophilic substitution reactions with all alkyl halides in which olefin formation is possible are almost invariably accompanied by more or less elimination to form olefins. The ratio of substitution to elimination in any given case is to a large extent governed by the nature of the alkyl halide (especially whether it is primary, secondary, or tertiary) and the nature of the nucleophile (especially its bulkiness and the relationship of its Brønsted basicity, or proton-abstracting ability, to its nucleophilicity). Elimination with olefin formation tends to increase with increasing bulkiness of the alkyl halide (primary < secondary < tertiary) and of the nucleophile, and with a high ratio of Brønsted basicity to nucleophilicity* in the nucleophile. Experimentally, however, even for a given nucleophile and alkyl halide, we can often exercise considerable control over the ratio of elimination to substitution, in whichever direction is desired. Choice of solvent, reactant concentrations, and temperature is important in this control.

Nucleophilic Displacements at Unsaturated Carbon

Some of the most interesting and important nucleophilic substitutions occur at carbon that is multiply-bonded to a

*As a simple example, we can say that $:\ddot{\underset{..}{\text{F}}}:^-$ has a much higher Brønsted basicity/nucleophilicity ratio than does $:\ddot{\underset{..}{\text{I}}}:^-$. Many of the special uses of hydrogen iodide in organic chemistry depend upon the fact that it permits the incorporation of a strong nucleophile, $:\ddot{\underset{..}{\text{I}}}:^-$, in a highly acidic system, H—I

highly electronegative element, commonly oxygen. Most familiar of these reactions are those involving the *carboxylic acids* ($R{-}\overset{\overset{O}{\|}}{C}{-}OH$) and their functional derivatives, the *acyl or acid chlorides** ($R{-}\overset{\overset{O}{\|}}{C}{-}Cl$), *acid anhydrides* ($R{-}\overset{\overset{O}{\|}}{C}{-}O{-}\overset{\overset{O}{\|}}{C}{-}R$), esters ($R{-}\overset{\overset{O}{\|}}{C}{-}OR'$), and amides ($R{-}\overset{\overset{O}{\|}}{C}{-}NH_2$)**. These compounds are all acid derivatives in which the OH of a carboxylic acid has been replaced by a Cl, $O{-}\overset{\overset{O}{\|}}{C}{-}R$, OR′, or NH_2 group. They all contain the acyl group, $R{-}\overset{\overset{O}{\|}}{C}$. In fact, they may all be regarded as substrates made up of the acid portion $R{-}\overset{\overset{O}{\|}}{C}{+}$, (an acylium ion) and the base portion $:\ddot{\underset{..}{Cl}}:^-$, $:\ddot{\underset{..}{O}}{-}\overset{\overset{O}{\|}}{C}{-}R^-$, $:\ddot{\underset{..}{O}}{-}H^-$, $:\ddot{\underset{..}{O}}{-}R^-$, or $H{-}\ddot{\underset{..}{N}}{-}H^-$.

All of these acid derivatives are prepared directly or indirectly from the corresponding acids, and much of the chemistry of the entire group deals with their conversion, one into another. The characteristic type reaction involved in these interconversions is *nucleophilic substitution* in which the Cl, $O{-}\overset{\overset{O}{\|}}{C}{-}R$, OH, OR, or NH_2 is replaced by some nucleophile. Three typical examples are shown in Table 5.3.

*Acid bromides and iodides are more expensive and difficult to prepare, and have no particular advantages over acid chlorides.

**One or both of the hydrogens shown in the general formula for amides can be alkyl groups.

TABLE 5.3. Typical Nucleophilic Substitutions at Unsaturated Carbon

Reaction	Nucleophile	Acyl Compound or Substrate		Substitution Product
(1) Hydrolysis of Acid Chlorides	$H{-}\ddot{\underset{..}{O}}{-}H$ +	$R{-}\overset{:O:}{\overset{\Vert}{C}}{-}\ddot{\underset{..}{Cl}}:$	$\rightleftharpoons$	$R{-}\overset{:O:}{\overset{\Vert}{C}}{-}\ddot{\underset{..}{O}}{-}H + H{-}\ddot{\underset{..}{Cl}}:$
(2) Esterification	$R'{-}\ddot{\underset{..}{O}}{-}H$ +	$R{-}\overset{:O:}{\overset{\Vert}{C}}{-}\ddot{\underset{..}{O}}{-}H$	$\rightleftharpoons$	$R{-}\overset{:O:}{\overset{\Vert}{C}}{-}\ddot{\underset{..}{O}}{-}R' + H{-}\ddot{\underset{..}{O}}{-}H$
(3) Ammonolysis of Acid Anhydrides	$H{-}\underset{H}{\overset{H}{N}}:$	$+\ R{-}\overset{:O:}{\overset{\Vert}{C}}{-}\ddot{\underset{..}{O}}{-}\overset{:O:}{\overset{\Vert}{C}}{-}R$	$\rightleftharpoons$	$R{-}\overset{:O:}{\overset{\Vert}{C}}{-}\underset{..}{\overset{H}{N}}{-}H + R{-}\overset{:O:}{\overset{\Vert}{C}}{-}\ddot{\underset{..}{O}}{-}H$

Note that the net change at the $\overset{O}{\overset{\Vert}{C}}$ carbon in the three reactions is the displacement in (1) of $:\ddot{\underset{..}{Cl}}:^-$ by $^-:\ddot{\underset{..}{O}}{-}H$, in (2) of $^-:\ddot{\underset{..}{O}}{-}H$ by $^-:\ddot{\underset{..}{O}}{-}R'$, and in (3) of $^-:\ddot{\underset{..}{O}}{-}\overset{O}{\overset{\Vert}{C}}{-}R$ by $:\underset{H}{\overset{H}{N}}:^-$. In general, the net change at carbon is displacement of one nucleophile, $Y:^-$, by another, $Z:^-$. These displacements occur much more facilely than do the corresponding nucleophilic displacements at saturated carbon.

The marked reactivity of acyl compounds is readily explainable electronically. The highly electronegative oxygen atom strongly attracts the mobile π electrons of the carbon-oxygen double bond toward itself, away from carbon. We can represent this diagrammatically simply by showing partial charges on the carbon and oxygen or, exaggerating the effect, by the hypothetical, completely-polarized structure:

$$\mathrm{R{-}\overset{\overset{:\ddot{O}:^{\delta-}}{\|}}{\underset{\delta+}{C}}{-}Y} \quad \text{or} \quad \mathrm{R{-}\overset{\overset{:\ddot{O}:^{\ominus}}{|}}{\underset{\oplus}{C}}{-}Y}$$

The significant result is this: the carbon is a highly electron-deficient, positive, or "acidic" center and is, therefore, strongly susceptible to nucleophilic attack. In fact, the pair of electrons supplied by the nucleophile can be accomodated by the carbon, i.e., a true bond can be formed, merely through a complete internal shift of the mobile π electrons from the carbon to the oxygen. This is evident from the accepted mechanism for the typical un-catalyzed nucleophilic substitution reaction of H—Z : with carbonyl compounds.*

$$\mathrm{H{-}\ddot{Z}:} + \mathrm{R{-}\overset{\overset{:O:^{\delta-}}{\|}}{\underset{\delta+}{C}}{-}Y} \rightleftharpoons \mathrm{R{-}\overset{\overset{\overset{H}{|}}{\overset{:\ddot{O}:}{|}}}{\underset{\underset{\ddot{Z}}{|}}{C}}{-}Y} \rightleftharpoons \mathrm{R{-}\overset{\overset{:O:}{\|}}{C}{-}\ddot{Z}:} + \mathrm{H{-}Y}$$

Nucleophilic Attack

With only four, rather than five, groups surrounding the carbon, the intermediate is also less strained sterically and,

*One of the intriguing aspects of an electronic analysis of the mechanism of almost any organic reaction is the variety of viewpoints from which the reaction may be interpreted. In the general nucleophilic substitution shown, for example, the $\overset{\overset{O}{\|}}{C}$ may be regarded as a type of electron-pair-carrier. In the first step nucleophile H—Z : displaces the electron pair from carbon completely onto oxygen; then in the second step an electron pair on oxygen displaces Y :⁻ at carbon. The over-all result is a much more facile displacement than would be achieved by direct one-step displacement of Y :⁻ by H—Z :.

therefore, more stable than the transition state (p. 84) for nucleophilic displacement at saturated carbon. The system can proceed from reactants to products by way of an intermediate that is relatively stable electronically and sterically. This provides the pathway for a facile displacement.

In fact, we might wonder why the reaction does not stop with the formation of the intermediate, as a simple nucleophilic addition (cf. pp. 70 and 99). Let's take a closer look at the structure of the reactive acyl compounds or substrates.

Note that on each of the various Y groups in $R-\overset{\overset{\textstyle :O:}{\|}}{C}-Y:$ there is at least one unshared electron pair. As a result, each acyl compound is actually a resonance hybrid receiving contributions from two types of resonance structures, (1) and (2):

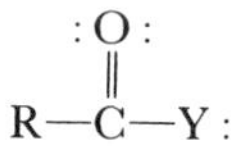

$$\underset{(1)}{R-\overset{\overset{\textstyle :O:}{\|}}{C}-Y:} \qquad\qquad \underset{(2)}{R-\overset{\overset{\textstyle :\ddot{O}:^{\ominus}}{|}}{C}=Y^{\oplus}}$$

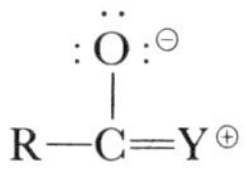

To the extent that structure (2) contributes to the resonance hybrid, it affords a degree of stabilization (resonance energy) that is completely lost in the saturated intermediate. More or less (depending upon the relative basicities of $:Z:^-$ and $:Y:^-$) of this resonance stabilization can be restored simply by loss of H—Y: from the intermediate. In other words, the intermediate is less stable, because of loss of resonance energy, than either $R-\overset{\overset{\textstyle O}{\|}}{C}-Y$ or $R-\overset{\overset{\textstyle O}{\|}}{C}-Z$.

As we might expect, the various nucleophilic displacements at unsaturated carbon differ markedly both in rate and in extent to which they proceed to completion. We would predict that the more *reactive the attacking nucleophile and the weaker the* *departing base,** the *faster should be the reaction,* and the *stronger the displacing base and the weaker the displaced base, the more complete should be the displacement at equilibrium.*

Because nucleophilicity and basicity run parallel in the series, we can confidently predict the conclusions about relative rate and extent of reaction summarized in Table 5.4.

All these predictions are richly verified by the experimental facts. Acid chlorides are by far the most reactive of the acyl compounds; they react rapidly and completely. With ammonia and acetyl chloride, for example, the reaction is violent. On the other hand, acid anhydrides react somewhat more slowly and less completely. Ethyl acetate reacts much more slowly, and under equilibrium conditions its reaction with any nucleophile in the list except ammonia is only very partial.† Similarly, it is impossible to prepare acid chlorides directly in good yield from any combination of reagents in Table 5.4 because chloride ion is too weak to displace any other base.

In fact, we can make the following generalization: under

*If you like to explore these relationships from several standpoints, you will enjoy toying with this idea: the more resonance structure (2) contributes to the true structure of the resonance hybrid the more it stabilizes R—C(=O)—Y and the more it decreases the positive or acid character of the carbon:

$$\underset{\delta+}{\mathrm{R{-}C}}(\overset{\delta-}{=\ddot{O}:})\mathrm{{-}Y:} \qquad \mathrm{R{-}C}(\mathrm{{-}\ddot{O}:^{\ominus}})\mathrm{{=}Y^{\oplus}}$$

Positive Charge is Shared by Y *through Resonance*

Because structure (2) depends upon electron-pair- donation by Y to C, its contribution should definitely increase with basicity of :Y:⁻. What does this suggest about the dependence of rate and extent of reaction upon the nature of Y?

†The K_{eq} of the reaction of ethyl acetate with ethyl alcohol is, of course, 1, but this reaction is not synthetically useful. On the other hand, with other alcohols, ROH, ethyl acetate undergoes ester interchange, a type of reaction which under controlled conditions can be extremely useful.

TABLE 5.4. Relative Rates and Extents of Nucleophilic Substitutions at Unsaturated Carbon

Nucleophile (↓ *Increasing Nucleophilicity—Increasing Rate of Reaction*)	Displacing Base (↓ *Increasing Basicity—Increasing Extent of Reaction*)	Acyl Compound or Substrate (↑ *Increasing Positive Charge at C—Increasing Rate of Reaction*)	Leaving Group (↑ *Decreasing Basicity—Increasing Rate and Extent of Reaction*)
$H{-}Z:$	$:Z:^-$	$R{-}C(=O){-}Y:$	$:Y:^-$
$H{-}\ddot{Cl}:$	$:\ddot{Cl}:^-$	$R{-}C(=\ddot{O}){-}\ddot{Cl}:$	$:\ddot{Cl}:^-$
$R{-}C(=\ddot{O}){-}\ddot{O}{-}H$	$R{-}C(=\ddot{O}){-}\ddot{O}:^-$	$R{-}C(=\ddot{O}){-}\ddot{O}{-}C(=\ddot{O}){-}R$	$:\ddot{O}{-}C(=\ddot{O}){-}R^-$
$H{-}\ddot{O}{-}H$	$H{-}\ddot{O}:^-$	$R{-}C(=\ddot{O}){-}\ddot{O}{-}H$	$:\ddot{O}{-}H^-$
$R{-}\ddot{O}{-}H$	$R{-}\ddot{O}:^-$	$R{-}C(=\ddot{O}){-}\ddot{O}R'$	$:\ddot{O}{-}R'^-$
$H{-}N(H)(H):$	$:N(H)(H):^-$	$R{-}C(=\ddot{O}){-}\ddot{N}(H){-}H$	$:\ddot{N}(H){-}H^-$

equilibrium conditions and barring the intervention of strong spatial or steric effects, any base will displace over 50 per cent ($K_{eq} > 1$) of any base above it in the base column (weaker base), to an extent suggested by the distance between the two bases in the column.

Thus the fairly rapid reaction of ethyl alcohol with acetyl chloride $\left(CH_3{-}C(=O){-}Cl\right)$ to form ethyl acetate $\left(CH_3{-}C(=O){-}O{-}C_2H_5,\right)$ in which $C_2H_5{-}\ddot{O}:^-$ replaces $:\ddot{Cl}:^-$, proceeds essentially to completion. The slow esterification of acetic acid with ethyl alcohol to form ethyl acetate ($C_2H_5{-}\ddot{O}:^-$ replacing $:\ddot{O}{-}H^-$), however, is only 2/3 complete at equilibrium when equimolar quantities of reactants are used ($K_{eq} = 4$).

Because many of the reactions suggested in Table 5.4 are slow and because equilibria are often unfavorable, chemists have devised all kinds of strategies both to increase the rate of the reactions and to drive them to completion. Theoretically, strong Brønsted acids should catalyze all the reactions by conversion of the acyl compounds to their conjugate acids, in which the carbon is even more "acidic" or vulnerable to nucleophilic attack:

$$\mathrm{R{-}\overset{\overset{\delta-}{:O:}}{\underset{\delta+}{C}}{-}Y} + \mathrm{H{-}A} \rightleftharpoons \mathrm{R{-}\overset{:\ddot{O}-H}{\underset{\oplus}{C}}{-}Y} + \mathrm{A:^-}$$

The fact is that strong mineral acids, HA, do catalyze all the reactions listed except those involving ammonia. Here they merely convert the nucleophile to its conjugate acid, NH_4^+, which cannot function as a nucleophile. On the other hand, the hydrolysis and alcoholysis of amides are driven to completion when run in acid medium, through conversion of ammonia to ammonium ion, which cannot participate in the reverse reaction.

In all cases, use of conditions in which the nucleophile H—Z: exists as its conjugate base, $:Z:^-$, should speed reaction, because $:Z:^-$ is always a stronger nucleophile than H—Z:. For example, carboxylic acids are weak nucleophiles at best, so acid anhydrides are best prepared by reaction of sodium carboxylate salts with acid chlorides:

$$\mathrm{R'{-}\overset{\overset{:O:}{\|}}{C}{-}\ddot{\underset{..}{O}}:^-} + \mathrm{R{-}\overset{\overset{:O:}{\|}}{C}{-}\ddot{\underset{..}{Cl}}:} \rightarrow \mathrm{R{-}\overset{\overset{:O:}{\|}}{C}{-}\ddot{\underset{..}{O}}{-}\overset{\overset{:O:}{\|}}{C}{-}R'} + \mathrm{:\ddot{\underset{..}{Cl}}:^-}$$

Stronger nucleophile than R—COOH.

On the other hand, use of ethoxide or amide ion in attempted nucleophilic substitution on a carboxylic acid merely converts the acid to its conjugate base, which as a stable anion is not attacked by nucleophiles. This suggests, however, that hydrolysis of all the various acid derivatives can be driven to completion by use of an alkaline medium, which converts the carboxylic acid product to its stable anion. Thus the saponification of esters (hydrolysis in alkaline medium) is irreversible:

$$\mathrm{H{-}\ddot{\underset{..}{O}}:^- + R{-}\overset{\overset{:O:}{\|}}{C}{-}\ddot{\underset{..}{O}}{-}R' \rightarrow R{-}\overset{\overset{:O:}{\|}}{C}{-}\ddot{\underset{..}{O}}:^- + R'{-}\ddot{\underset{..}{O}}{-}H}$$

Careful study of Table 5.4 will lead to a large number of further interesting predictions. Try some yourself—then check them in a good textbook of organic chemistry.

Reactions of acyl compounds with additional nucleophiles form the basis for many other important reactions in organic chemistry. Just a few of the important type reactions are illustrated by means of specific examples in Table 5.5.

Nucleophilic Addition Reactions

Among the most important and interesting organic compounds are those containing a carbon linked to a single hetero-atom (not C or H) by a multiple bond. Most familiar are the carbonyl compounds—the aldehydes ($\mathrm{R{-}\overset{\overset{O}{\|}}{C}{-}H}$), such as acetaldehyde ($\mathrm{CH_3{-}\overset{\overset{O}{\|}}{C}{-}H}$), and the ketones ($\mathrm{R{-}\overset{\overset{O}{\|}}{C}{-}R'}$), such as acetone ($\mathrm{CH_3{-}\overset{\overset{O}{\|}}{C}{-}CH_3}$).

In these compounds, the π-electron pair is pulled strongly toward oxygen away from carbon:

TABLE 5.5. Additional Types of Nucleophilic Substitutions at Unsaturated Carbon

	Acyl Compound or Substrate	Nucleophile	Substitution Product
	$R{-}C(=O) \mid {-}Y$	$:Z^-$	$R{-}C(=O){-}Z$ (or conjugate base)
Claisen Condensation	$CH_3{-}C(=O) \mid {-}OC_2H_5$	$^{\ominus}:CH_2{-}C(=O){-}OC_2H_5$	$CH_3{-}C(=O){-}CH_2{-}C(=O){-}OC_2H_5$
Cleavage of β-Ketoesters	$CH_3{-}C(=O) \mid {-}CH_2{-}C(=O){-}O{-}C_6H_5$*	$^{\ominus}:\ddot{O}{-}H$	$CH_3{-}C(=O){-}\ddot{O}:^{\ominus}$
Haloform Splitting	$CH_3{-}C(=O) \mid {-}CI_3$*	$^{\ominus}:\ddot{O}{-}H$	$CH_3{-}C(=O){-}\ddot{O}:^{\ominus}$
Acylation of Malonic Ester	$CH_3{-}C(=O) \mid {-}Cl$	$^{\ominus}:CH({-}C(=O){-}OC_2H_5)_2$	$CH_3{-}C(=O){-}CH({-}C(=O){-}OC_2H_5)_2$
First Step in Synthesis of t-Alcohols from Esters	$CH_3{-}C(=O) \mid {-}OC_2H_5$	$R{-}CH_2:^-[Mg^{++}, Br^-]$	$CH_3{-}C(=O){-}CH_2{-}R$

*Where a C—C bond is broken, the displaced group $Y:^-$ is a much weaker base than a simple hydrocarbon carbanion such as methide ion.

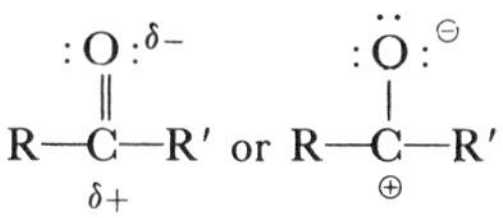

$$\overset{:\mathrm{O}:^{\delta-}}{\underset{\delta+}{\mathrm{R{-}\overset{\|}{C}{-}R'}}} \quad \text{or} \quad \overset{:\ddot{\mathrm{O}}:^{\ominus}}{\underset{\oplus}{\mathrm{R{-}\overset{|}{C}{-}R'}}}$$

As a result the carbon is an electron-deficient or acidic center* and is highly susceptible to nucleophilic attack—especially because the carbonyl portion of the molecule is flat or planar, and the attacking nucleophile has free access from either direction perpendicular to the plane of the carbonyl group. It is this susceptibility to attack by electron-donor, nucleophilic reagents that dictates much of the chemistry of the carbonyl and related compounds (such as nitriles, RCN).

As the nucleophile attacks, the carbonyl compound can accommodate the incoming electron pair merely by a complete polarization or internal shift of the π electron pair from carbon to oxygen.** Addition of proton to the oxygen then gives a relatively stable tetrahedral addition compound, just as was the case for the acid derivatives (p. 94). But, in aldehydes and ketones, neither the hydrogen nor the carbon bonded to carbonyl carbon has an unshared electron pair which would permit the type of resonance that characterizes the acid derivatives. For example,

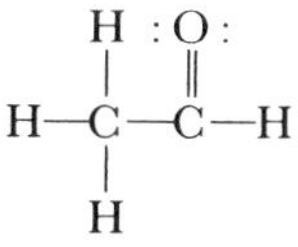

$$\mathrm{H{-}\underset{H}{\overset{H}{C}}{-}\overset{:O:}{\overset{\|}{C}}{-}H} \quad \text{can show no structure corresponding to} \quad \mathrm{H{-}\underset{H}{\overset{H}{C}}{-}\overset{:\ddot{O}:^{\ominus}}{\overset{|}{C}}{=}\overset{\oplus}{\underset{\cdot\cdot}{O}}{-}CH_3}$$

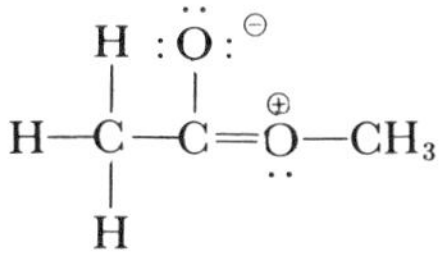

As a result, there is no great loss of resonance energy in the addition product, which is therefore reasonably stable compared to the starting aldehyde or ketone. From another point of view, none of the nucleophiles commonly employed

*In fact, aldehydes and ketones can actually be classified as Lewis acids (see p. 70).

**We can very logically view this step as a nucleophilic displacement of a pair of electrons at carbon.

under ordinary conditions is a sufficiently strong base to displace either the powerful base hydride ion (H :$^-$) or the equally strong hydrocarbon carbanion (R :$^-$). In other words the *addition product* is the *final product* in the typical reaction of carbonyl compounds; in fact, in most reactions it exists in equilibrium with the starting materials. Thus the characteristic reaction of aldehydes and ketones in an over-all sense is *nucleophilic addition.*

Using :N$^-$ or :N—H to designate the attacking nucleophilic, we can represent the accepted mechanisms for nucleophilic addition to aldehydes and ketones as follows:

For Anionic Nucleophilic Attack

$$\underset{\text{Planar}}{R^1(R)C{=}O} + {:}N^- \rightleftharpoons \underset{\text{Tetrahedral}}{R^1{-}C(N)(R){-}\ddot{\underset{..}{O}}{:}^{\ominus}} \xrightarrow[\text{HOH}]{\text{H : N or}} R^1{-}C(N)(R){-}\ddot{O}{-}H + \begin{matrix}{:}N^- \\ \text{or} \\ {:}\ddot{\underset{..}{O}}{-}H^-\end{matrix}$$

For Molecular Nucleophilic Attack

$$R^1(R)C{=}O + {:}N{-}H \rightleftharpoons R^1{-}C(\overset{\oplus}{N}{-}H)(R){-}\ddot{\underset{..}{O}}{:}^{\ominus} \rightleftharpoons R^1{-}C(N{:})(R){-}\ddot{O}{-}H$$

The over-all reaction in each case, is the addition of N—H to the carbonyl group, although under alkaline or often even neutral conditions, the attacking nucleophile is the anion :N$^-$, rather than N—H.

As a general rule, the addition reactions proceed both faster and also farther to completion the more electron-deficient or acidic is the carbonyl carbon and the less bulky are the groups attached to it.*

*There are notable exceptions, in which rate and extent of reaction do not parallel each other.

TABLE 5.6. Some Nucleophilic Additions of N—H to Carbonyl Compounds.

Reaction	Nucleophile	Addition Product
Cyanohydrin Synthesis	CN^-	$-C(OH)-CN$
Grignard Synthesis of Alcohols	$R:^-(Mg^{++},X^-)$	$-C(O^-)-R$, Mg^{++}, X^- $\xrightarrow{HOH}$ $-C(OH)-R$
Oxime Synthesis	H_2N-O-H	$-C(HO)-N(H)-OH$ $\xrightarrow{-HOH}$ $-C=N-OH$
Phenylhydrazone Synthesis	$H_2N-NH-C_6H_5$	$-C(HO)-N(H)-NH-C_6H_5$ $\xrightarrow{-HOH}$ $-C=N-NH-C_6H_5$
Aldol Condensation	$^{\ominus}:C-C=O$	$-C(OH)-C-C=O$
Knoevenagel Reaction	$^{\ominus}:CH(-COOC_2H_5)_2$	$-C(HO)-C(H)(-COOC_2H_5)_2$ $\xrightarrow{-HOH}$ $-C=C(-COOC_2H_5)_2$

Since alkyl groups are both more electron-releasing (less electronegative) and much more bulky than hydrogen, ketones are considerably less reactive than aldehydes. In fact, for certain typical reactions, such as the hydrogen cyanide and sodium bisulfite additions, the equilibrium in the cases of ketones containing bulky secondary or tertiary groups, which are even more electron-releasing than primary groups, is so unfavorable that the reactions are not synthetically useful. On the other hand, in a number of typical reactions (such as the synthesis of oximes and phenylhydrazones, and the Knoevenagel reaction) the initially-formed addition product loses a molecule of water irreversibly. This, of course, drives the forward reaction to completion, and a good yield of the final unsaturated product is formed even from sterically hindered ketones, although the reaction may be very slow.

Many nucleophilic addition reactions are acid or base catalyzed. An acid catalyst is effective if it can coordinate with the carbonyl oxygen, thereby increasing the acidity of the carbonyl carbon, without reacting preferentially with the nucleophile. Thus, for Brønsted acid catalysts the desired function is as follows:

$$\begin{matrix} R \\ & \overset{\delta+}{C} = \overset{\delta-}{\ddot{O}:} \;\; H{-}A \\ R' \end{matrix} \rightleftharpoons \begin{matrix} R \\ & \overset{\oplus}{C} - \ddot{\underset{..}{O}}{-}H + A:^{-} \\ R' \end{matrix}$$

C is now more "positive" or acidic

A base catalyst usually functions by displacing the reactive base or nucleophile, in concentration at least sufficient for reaction, from its combination with proton (as in the aldol condensation and the Knoevenagel reaction). Table 5.6 shows in summary form a few of the important nucleophilic additions to carbonyl compounds.

chapter six

ACID DISPLACEMENTS AND ADDITIONS

(or, The Plot Thickens)

All Brønsted protolyses are base displacements (p. 73). And in a broad sense, nucleophilic substitutions, eliminations, and nucleophilic additions can be brought under the base displacement tent. But are there any acid displacements?

The fact is that, although less numerous, displacements of one Lewis acid by another constitute a fundamental type reaction of great importance. Consider the high temperature reaction of silica with carbonates, important in metallurgy:

Acid displaces acid

Base | Acid

$$(SiO_2)_x + X{:}\ddot{\underset{..}{O}}{-}\ \Big|\ \overset{:O:}{\overset{\|}{C}}{-}\ddot{\underset{..}{O}}{:} \longrightarrow \left[{:}\ddot{\underset{..}{O}}{-}\overset{:O:}{\overset{\|}{Si}}{-}\ddot{\underset{..}{O}}{:}\right]_x + X\ \overset{:O:}{\overset{\|}{C}}{=}\ddot{\underset{..}{O}}$$

The ionization of aluminum chloride in phosgene, to give a solution which liberates carbon monoxide in reaction with active metals, is another example of acid displacement:

Acid displaces acid

Base | Acid

$$:\ddot{Cl}{-}AlCl_3 \text{ (} :\ddot{Cl}:-Al(-\ddot{Cl}:)_2 \text{)} + :\ddot{Cl}:^- \,|\, \overset{+}{C}(=O)-\ddot{Cl}: \longrightarrow [:\ddot{Cl}-Al(\ddot{Cl}:)_3]^- + \overset{+}{C}(=\ddot{O})-\ddot{Cl}:$$

Acid Displacements in Acid Catalyses

The role of acid catalysts in many reactions is to displace, at least in sufficient concentration for further reaction, the reacting acid in the main reaction. In the Lucas test for secondary and tertiary alcohols, the acid catalyst zinc chloride displaces carbonium ion (R^+) for reaction with chloride ion:

Acid catalyst displaces reacting acid

$$:\ddot{Cl}-Zn-\ddot{Cl}: + H-\ddot{O}^{-}\,|\,{}^{+}R \rightleftharpoons :\ddot{Cl}-\underset{|}{\overset{:\ddot{Cl}:^-}{Zn}}-\ddot{O}H + R^+$$

Additional examples of the function of acid catalysts in displacing the acids involved in reaction are shown in Table 6.1.

Electrophilic Displacements

All four of the displaced acids in Table 6.1 are powerful Lewis acids—so powerful in fact that they attack aromatic compounds such as benzene (Kekulé structure $\longleftrightarrow$ Kekulé structure, or ring with dotted circle) and effect, as the over-all reaction, displacement of H^+. The benzene ring system is highly stabilized through resonance, and the cloud of π electrons above and below the plane of the ring is much more strongly involved in bond formation than are the π electrons in an olefin such as ethylene ($CH_2{=}CH_2$). Toward such powerful electron-pair acceptors as bromine cation, nitronium ion, carbonium ions, and acylium ions, as well as sulfur trioxide, however, benzene

TABLE 6.1. The Role of Acid Catalysts in Displacing the Actual Acids Involved in Aromatic Bromination, Nitration, and Friedel-Crafts Alkylation and Acylation.

Acid		displaces			reacting acid
:Br—Fe(—:Br:)(—:Br:)	+	:Br:$^-$ — :Br:$^+$	⇌	:Br—Fe(—Br:)(—:Br:)—Br: $^-$ +	:Br$^+$ Bromine cation
H—O—S(=O)(—O:)—O—H	+	H—O:$^-$ — :O=N$^+$—O:	⇌	HSO_4^- + H_2O +	:O=N$^+$—O: Nitronium ion
:Cl—Al(—:Cl:)(—:Cl:)	+	:Cl:$^-$ — $\overset{+}{R}$	⇌	:Cl—Al(—Cl:)(—:Cl:)—Cl: $^-$ +	R$^+$ Carbonium ion
:Cl—Al(—:Cl:)(—:Cl:)	+	:Cl:$^-$ — :O=$\overset{+}{C}$—R	⇌	:Cl—Al(—Cl:)(—:Cl:)—Cl: $^-$ +	R—C$^+$(=O:) Acylium ion

can serve as a source of an electron pair, or as a *base.* The reagents which attack benzene are electron-deficient or acidic. In general, electron-pair seeking reagents, whether they are true Lewis acids or whether they can accommodate a pair of electrons only as a base is simultaneously displaced, are called *electrophilic (Greek,* electron-loving) *reagents* or *electrophiles.*

For reaction with benzene (and other aromatic compounds) the four cationic electrophiles named are released for reaction by acid displacement as shown in Table 6.1. Then, according to the accepted mechanism for electrophilic substitution, these electrophiles attack the benzene ring, bonding to carbon through one pair of electrons from the π cloud to form an *activated complex.* When the electrophile is a cation, E^+, the activated complex is also a cation (a phenonium ion)

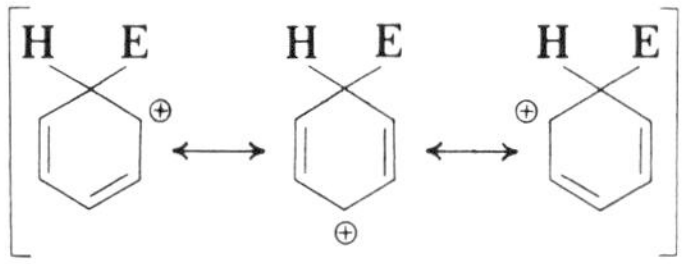

with the positive charge dispersed over the ring, especially at the para and the two ortho positions. Without the stabilization brought about by this charge distribution, the ion probably could not be formed at all.

The ion is still, however, unstable compared to benzene, which is an unusually stable resonance hybrid. But simply through loss of proton from the activated complex, $C_6H_6E^+$, the benzene resonance system can be restored, and this is exactly what occurs.

In each case, then, the over-all reaction at carbon is a displacement by the electrophile E^+ of the acid H^+, and we call this type of reaction *electrophilic substitution.* This is the characteristic type reaction of benzene and all other aromatic compounds. Pertinent facts about these four important electrophilic substitutions as applied to benzene are listed in Table 6.2.

In the sulfonation reaction with SO_3, the fundamental mechanism is the same, but the activated complex bears no total charge, and in effect the proton is shifted intramolecularly:

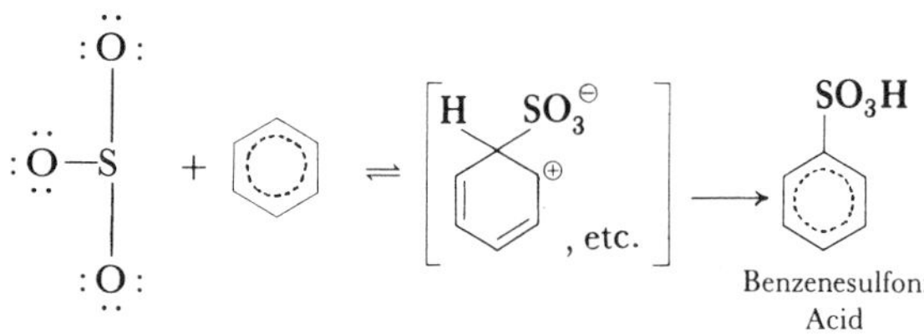

, etc.

Benzenesulfonic Acid

TABLE 6.2. Four Important Electrophilic Substitutions as Applied to Benzene—Bromination, Nitration, Alkylation, and Acylation.

Electrophile, E^+	Activated Complex (Phenonium Type Ion)	Proton Acceptor	Product
$:\ddot{\underset{..}{Br}}^+$	$C_6H_6—Br^+$	$\xrightarrow{FeBr_4^-}$	$C_6H_5—Br + FeBr_3 + HBr$ Bromobenzene
NO_2^+	$C_6H_6—NO_2^+$	$\xrightarrow{HSO_4^-}$	$C_6H_5—NO_2 + H_2SO_4$ Nitrobenzene
R^+	$C_6H_6—R^+$	$\xrightarrow{AlCl_4^-}$	$C_6H_5—R + AlCl_3 + HCl$ An alkylbenzene
$R—\overset{\overset{O}{\Vert}}{C}{}^+$	$C_6H_6—\overset{\overset{O}{\Vert}}{C}—R^+$	$\xrightarrow{AlCl_4^-}$	$C_6H_5—\overset{\overset{O}{\Vert}}{C}—R + AlCl_3 + HCl$ An Aromatic Ketone

Predictions about the effect of a substituent already present on a benzene ring on the rate of further substitution are based upon the electron-releasing effect of the substituent in stabilizing, or its electron-withdrawing effect in de-stabilizing, the activated complex. The effect of any substituent already present in dictating the position on the ring at which further substitution will occur can also be predicted. It is found that proton will be displaced primarily at that position on the ring which, on the basis of the resonance effect brought about by the substituent, is associated with the most stable of the possible activated complexes.

In such an analysis, the conclusions are largely equivalent to predictions one would make by assuming that an activating substituent is one which enhances electron-availability (basicity) of the ring, and that substitution will occur at the position where electron-availability is most enhanced.

On the other hand, a de-activating group turns out to be one whose over-all effect is depletion of electron-availability (basicity) on the ring, and substitution will occur largely at the position where electron-availability is least depleted.

Electrophilic Additions

Much more readily available than the electrons in the π electron cloud above and below the plane of the ring in benzene are the loosely-held electrons forming the π bond in an olefin such as ethylene, $CH_2{=}CH_2$ (or the π bonds in an alkyne such as acetylene, $H{-}C{\equiv}C{-}H$). In other words, the olefins and alkynes are considerably stronger bases than are the aromatic compounds. As a result, a host of electrophiles, weaker than the Lewis acids just discussed, attack olefins and alkynes. For example, typical electrophiles which react with olefins are Cl_2, Br_2, ICl, IBr, HI, HBr, HCl, H_2SO_4, HNO_3, H_3O^+, HOCl, NOCl, and many others.

All may be regarded as coordinated complexes with a strong acid portion E^+ and a base portion $B{:}^-$ or $B{:}$. In the first, and presumably slow and rate-determining, step of the accepted mechanism, the acid portion bonds through the π electron pair of the olefin to form a type of carbonium ion

$$\begin{array}{c} \; | \quad\; | \\ -\mathrm{C}-\mathrm{C}- \\ \; | \quad\; \oplus \\ \mathrm{E} \quad\;\; \end{array}$$

, with simultaneous displacement of $B{:}^-$ or $B{:}$ from E^+. The carbonium ion thus formed is, in every case, an exceedingly reactive and unstable transient species. As a powerful electrophile, it can add $B{:}^-$ or $B{:}$ to form

$$\begin{array}{c} \; | \quad\; | \\ -\mathrm{C}-\mathrm{C}- \\ \; | \quad\; | \\ \mathrm{E} \quad \mathrm{B} \end{array}$$

, which has two strong σ bonds in place of the one weak π bond in the original olefin. As you would suppose, then, this is exactly what happens—in other words, the characteristic reactions of the olefins are electrophilic additions.

As applied to ethylene, for example, the addition of hydrogen iodine and of chlorine can be pictured as follows:

$$\begin{array}{c} \mathrm{H} \quad \mathrm{H} \\ | \quad\;\; | \\ \mathrm{C}{=}\mathrm{C} \\ | \quad\;\; | \\ \mathrm{H} \quad \mathrm{H} \end{array} + \mathrm{H}{-}\ddot{\underset{..}{\mathrm{I}}}{:} \rightleftharpoons \mathrm{H}{-}\begin{array}{c} \mathrm{H} \quad \mathrm{H} \\ | \quad\;\; | \\ \mathrm{C}{-}\mathrm{C}^{\oplus} \\ | \quad\;\; | \\ \mathrm{H} \quad \mathrm{H} \end{array} + {:}\ddot{\underset{..}{\mathrm{I}}}{:}^- \rightarrow \mathrm{H}{-}\begin{array}{c} \mathrm{H} \quad \mathrm{H} \\ | \quad\;\; | \\ \mathrm{C}{-}\mathrm{C} \\ | \quad\;\; | \\ \mathrm{H} \quad \mathrm{H} \end{array}{-}\ddot{\underset{..}{\mathrm{I}}}{:}$$

$$\mathrm{H_2C{=}CH_2} + :\ddot{\mathrm{Cl}}{-}\ddot{\mathrm{Cl}}: \rightleftharpoons :\ddot{\mathrm{Cl}}{-}\mathrm{CH_2}{-}\overset{\oplus}{\mathrm{C}}\mathrm{H_2} + :\ddot{\mathrm{Cl}}:^{-} \rightarrow :\ddot{\mathrm{Cl}}{-}\mathrm{CH_2}{-}\mathrm{CH_2}{-}\ddot{\mathrm{Cl}}:$$

Careful studies on the relative rates of addition of hydrogen halides to olefins have led to the conclusion that the reactions are faster, the more acidic the electrophile and the greater the electron availability in the olefin:

$$\mathrm{HI > HBr > HCl}$$

$$\mathrm{(CH_3)_2C{=}CH_2 > CH_3{-}CH{=}CH_2 > CH_2{=}CH_2 > CH_2{=}CHCl}$$

The rate-determining step in the addition of hydrogen halides may be looked upon simply as proton transfer from the acid HX to the base olefin, or as the base displacement of $:\ddot{\underset{..}{\mathrm{X}}}:^-$ by olefin. Hence, it is to be expected that the strongest acid (HI), which contains the weakest base (I^-), would be the most reactive.

Similarly, the rate of reaction should increase with an increase in π-electron availability (basicity) of the olefin. This, in turn, increases with an increase in the number of electron-releasing alkyl groups attached to the doubly bonded carbon atoms, but decreases with the introduction of an electronegative atom such as a halogen.

For an unsymmetrical olefin, the first step occurs in a manner to give the more stable carbonium ion. This rule predicts the direction of addition of unsymmetrical reagents to unsymmetrical double bonds. For example, in the addition of hydrogen chloride to the two unsymmetrical olefins $(CH_3)_2C{=}CH_2$ and $CH_3{-}CH{=}CH_2$, the relative stability of the two possible carbonium ions in each case is as follows:

$$\mathrm{(CH_3)_2\overset{\oplus}{C}{-}CH_3 > (CH_3)_2CH{-}\overset{\oplus}{C}H_2}$$

$$\mathrm{CH_3{-}\overset{\oplus}{C}H{-}CH_3 > CH_3{-}CH_2{-}\overset{\oplus}{C}H_2}$$

The addition of HCl to the olefins, therefore, produces the alkyl chloride $(CH_3)_2{-}\overset{\overset{\large Cl}{|}}{C}{-}CH_3$ rather than $(CH_3)_2{-}CH{-}CH_2Cl$, and $CH_3{-}CHCl{-}CH_3$ rather than $CH_3{-}CH_2{-}CH_2Cl$.

This also suggests a more general method for looking at the effect of substituents at the doubly-bonded carbons on reaction rates. The faster addition is the one which proceeds through the more stable carbonium ion. For the olefins listed, the stability of the corresponding carbonium ions, and therefore the rate of electrophilic addition, decreases in the order

$$(CH_3)_2C{=}CH_2 > CH_3{-}CH{=}CH_2 > CH_2{=}CH_2$$

$$(CH_3)_2{-}\overset{\oplus}{C}{-}CH_3 > CH_3{-}\overset{\oplus}{C}H{-}CH_3 > CH_3{-}\overset{\oplus}{C}H_2$$

By means of these acid-base principles, we can correlate, systematize, and predict countless facts of organic chemistry. But our purpose here is not to teach all of organic chemistry. One aim, rather, is to help those of you who are planning its study to appreciate the compelling beauty and fascination of the well-developed intellectual framework upon which modern organic chemistry is constructed.

INDEX

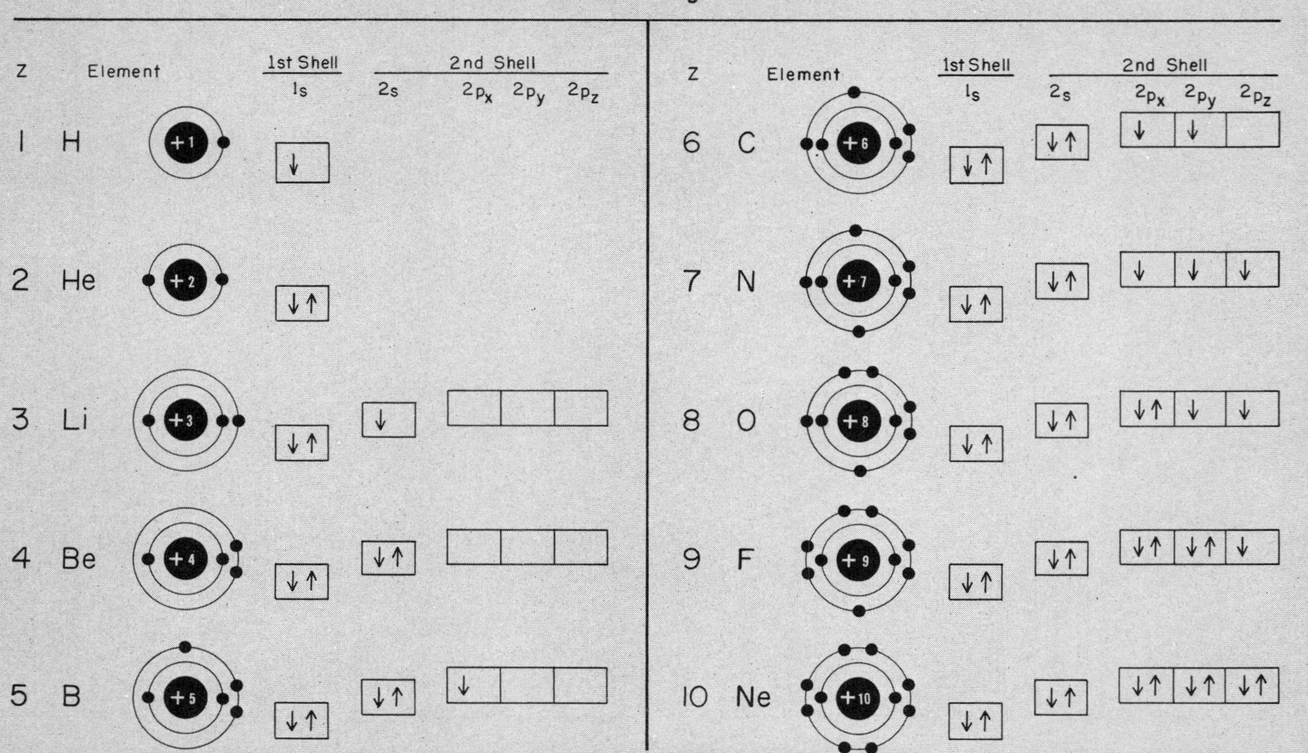
Electronic Configurations
Z
Element
1st Shell
1s
2nd Shell
2s
$2p_x$
$2p_y$
$2p_z$
1 H
+1
2 He
+2
3 Li
+3
4 Be
+4
5 B
+5
6 C
+6
7 N
+7
8 O
+8
9 F
+9
10 Ne
+10